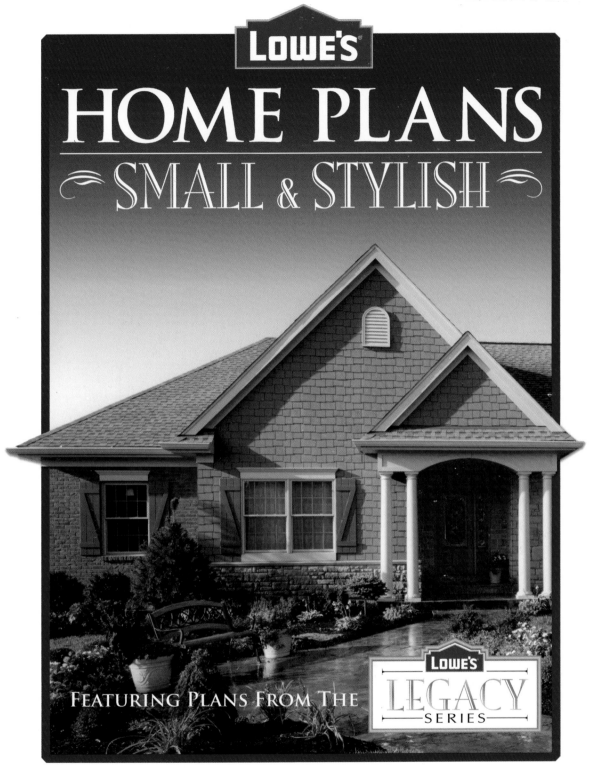

LOWE'S

HOME PLANS

SMALL & STYLISH

FEATURING PLANS FROM THE **LOWE'S LEGACY SERIES**

HDA

COVER HOME - The house shown on the front cover is
Plan #535-065L-0103 and is featured on page 13.
Photo courtesy of Studer Residential Design.

LOWE'S LEGACY SERIES: SMALL & STYLISH HOME PLANS
is published by HDA, Inc., 944 Anglum Road, St. Louis, MO, 63042.
All rights reserved. Reproduction in whole or in part without written
permission of the publisher is prohibited. Printed in U.S.A. © 2006.
Artist drawings and photos shown in this publication may vary
slightly from the actual working drawings. Some photos are shown
in mirror reverse. Please refer to the floor plan for accurate layout.

ISBN-13: 978-1-58678-064-7
ISBN-10: 1-58678-064-6

Current Printing

10 9 8 7 6 5 4 3

HDA, Inc.
944 Anglum Rd.
St. Louis, Missouri 63042
corporate website - www.hdainc.com

HOME PLANS
SMALL & STYLISH

CONTENTS

It's what separates you from the have knots.

LESS WANE, LESS WARP, AND FEWER KNOTS.

Top Choice lumber is hand selected at the mill and quality is verified by third-party inspectors. Plus, our treated lumber has a limited lifetime warranty against rot and decay. So whether you're adding a deck or a room, insist on Top Choice for your next project.

CERTIFIED QUALITY
TOP CHOICE®
LUMBER PRODUCTS

EXCLUSIVELY AT:

LOWE'S
Let's Build Something Together™

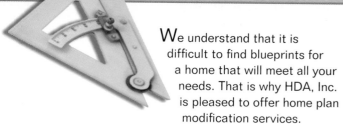

We understand that it is difficult to find blueprints for a home that will meet all your needs. That is why HDA, Inc. is pleased to offer home plan modification services.

Typical home plan modifications include:

- Changing foundation type
- Adding square footage to a plan
- Changing the entry into a garage
- Changing a two-car garage to a three-car garage or making a garage larger
- Redesigning kitchen, baths, and bedrooms
- Changing exterior elevations
- Or most other home plan modifications

Home plan modifications we cannot make include:

- Reversing the plans
- Adapting/engineering plans to meet your local building codes
- Combining parts of two different plans (due to copyright laws)

Our plan modification service is easy to use. Simply:

1. Decide on the modifications you want. For the most accurate quote, be as detailed as possible and refer to rooms in the same manner as the floor plan (i.e. if the floor plan refers to a "den" then use "den" in your description). Including a sketch of the modified floor plan is always helpful.

2. Complete and e-mail the modification request form that can be found online at www.houseplansandmore.com.

3. Within two business days, you will receive your quote. Quotes do not include the cost of the reproducible masters required for our designer to legally make changes.

4. Call to accept the quote and purchase the reproducible masters. For example, if your quote is $850 and the reproducible masters for your plan are $800, your order total will be $1650 plus two shipping and handling charges (one to ship the reproducible masters to our designer and one to ship the modified plans to you).

5. Our designer will send you up to three drafts to verify your initial changes. Extra costs apply after the third draft. If additional changes are made that alter the original request, extra charges may be incurred.

6. Once you approve a draft with the final changes, we then make the changes to the reproducible masters by adding additional sheets. The original reproducible masters (with no changes) plus your new changed sheets will be shipped to you.

Other Important Information:

- Plans cannot be redrawn in reverse format. All modifications will be made to match the reproducible master's original layout. Once you receive the plans, you can make reverse copies at your local blueprint shop.
- Our staff designer will provide the first draft for your review within 4 weeks (plus shipping time) of receiving your order.
- You will receive up to three drafts to review before your original changes are modified. The first draft will totally encompass all modifications based on your original request. Additional changes not included in your original request will be charged separately at an hourly rate of $75 or a flat quoted rate.
- Modifications will be drawn on a separate sheet with the changes shown and a note to see the main sheet for details. For example, a floor plan sheet from the original set (i.e. Sheet 3) would be followed by a new floor plan sheet with changes (i.e. Sheet A-3).
- Plans are drawn to meet national building codes. Modifications will not be drawn to any particular state or county codes, thus we cannot guarantee that the revisions will meet your local building codes. You may be required to have a local architect or designer review the plans in order to have them comply with your state or county building codes.
- Time and cost estimates are good for 90 calendar days.
- All modification requests need to be submitted in writing. Verbal requests will not be accepted.

2 EASY STEPS FOR FAST SERVICE

1. Visit www.houseplansandmore.com to download the modification request form.

2. E-mail the completed form to customize@hdainc.com or fax to 913-856-7751

If you are not able to access the internet, please call 1-877-379-3420
(Monday-Friday, 8am-5pm CST)

Choosing a home plan is an exciting but difficult task. Many factors play a role in what home plan is best for you and your family. To help you get started, we have pinpointed some of the major factors to consider when searching for your dream home. Take the time to evaluate your family's needs and you will have an easier time sorting through all of the home plans offered in this book.

BUDGET: The first thing to consider is your budget. Many items take part in this budget, from ordering the blueprints to the last doorknob purchased. Once you have found your dream home plan, visit your local Lowe's store to get a cost-to-build estimate to ensure that the finished product is still within your cost range.

FAMILY LIFESTYLE: After your budget is deciphered, you need to assess you and your family's lifestyle needs. Think about the stage of life you are at now, and what stages you will be going through in the future. Ask yourself questions to figure out how much room you need now and if you will need room for expansion. Are you married? Do you have children? How many children do you plan on having? Are you an empty-nester?

Incorporate in your planning any frequent guests you may have, including elderly parents, grandchildren or adult children who may live with you.

Does your family entertain a lot? If so, think about the rooms you will need to do so. Will you need both formal and informal spaces? Do you need a gourmet kitchen? Do you need a game room and/or a wet bar?

FLOOR PLAN LAYOUTS: When looking through our home plans, imagine yourself walking through the house. Consider the flow from the entry to the living, sleeping and gathering areas. Does the layout ensure privacy for the master bedroom? Does the garage enter near the kitchen for easy unloading? Does the placement of the windows provide enough privacy from any neighboring properties? Do you plan on using furniture you already have? Will this furniture fit in the appropriate rooms? When you find a plan you want to purchase, be sure to picture yourself actually living in it.

Experts in the field suggest that the best way to determine your needs is to begin by listing everything you like or dislike about your current home.

EXTERIOR SPACES: There are many different home styles ranging from Traditional to Contemporary. Flip through and find which style most appeals to you and the neighborhood in which you plan to build. Also think of your site and how the entire house will fit on this site. Picture any landscaping you plan on incorporating into the design. Using your imagination is key when choosing a home plan.

Choosing a home plan can be an intimidating experience. Asking yourself these questions before you get started on the search will help you through the process. With our large selection of multiple styles we are certain you will find your dream home in the following pages.

THE LOWE'S LEGACY SERIES

LEG·A·CY: SOMETHING THAT IS HANDED DOWN OR REMAINS FOR GENERATIONS

HDA, Inc. is proud to introduce to you the Lowe's Legacy Series. The home plans in this collection carry on the Lowe's tradition of quality and expertise, and will continue to do so for many generations.

Choosing a home plan can be a daunting task. With the Legacy Series, we will set your mind at ease. Selecting a plan from this group will ensure a home designed with the Lowe's standard of excellence, creating a dream home for you and your family.

This collection of Legacy Series plans includes our most popular small and stylish home plans. Browse through the pages to discover a home with the options and special characteristics you need.

Along with one-of-a-kind craftsmanship, all Legacy Series home plans offer industry-leading material lists. These accurate material lists will save you a considerable amount of time and money, providing you with the quantity, dimensions and descriptions of the major building materials necessary to construct your home. You'll get faster and more accurate bids from your contractor while saving money by paying for only the materials you need.

The Lowe's Legacy Series is the perfect place to start your search for the home of your dreams. You will find the expected beauty you want and the functional efficiency you need, all designed with unmatched quality.

Turn the page and begin the wonderful journey of finding your new home.

Photos clockwise from top: 535-065L-0074, page 20; 535-022D-0018, page 15; 535-022D-0007, page 33; 535-051L-0141, page 28.

SPECIAL FEATURES

1,556 total square feet of living area

A compact home with all the amenities

Country kitchen combines practicality with access to other areas for eating and entertaining

A three-sided fireplace joins the dining and living areas

A plant shelf and vaulted ceiling highlight the master bedroom

3 bedrooms, 2 1/2 baths, 2-car garage

Basement foundation

First Floor
834 sq. ft.

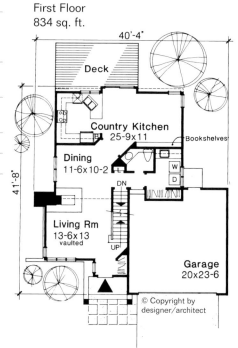

Second Floor
722 sq. ft.

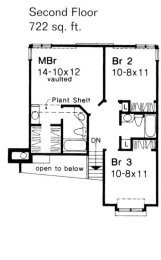

© Copyright by designer/architect

SPECIAL FEATURES

1,351 total square feet of living area

Roof lines and vaulted ceilings
make this home appear larger

Central fireplace provides a focal
point for the dining and living areas

Master bedroom features a roomy
window seat and a walk-in closet

Loft can easily be converted
to a third bedroom

2 bedrooms, 2 1/2 baths, 2-car garage

Basement foundation

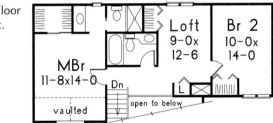

Second Floor
677 sq. ft.

Loft
9-0x
12-6

Br 2
10-0x
14-0

MBr
11-8x14-0

Dn

vaulted

open to below

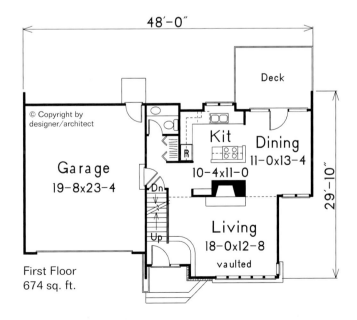

48'-0"

Deck

© Copyright by
designer/architect

Kit
10-4x11-0

Dining
11-0x13-4

Garage
19-8x23-4

Dn

29'-10"

Living
18-0x12-8
vaulted

Up

First Floor
674 sq. ft.

SPECIAL FEATURES

1,475 total square feet of living area

Family room features a high ceiling and prominent corner fireplace

Kitchen with island counter and garden window makes a convenient connection between the family and dining rooms

Hallway leads to three bedrooms all with large walk-in closets

Covered breezeway joins the main house and garage

Full-width covered porch entry lends a country touch

3 bedrooms, 2 baths, 2-car detached side entry garage

Slab foundation, drawings also include crawl space foundation

Side View

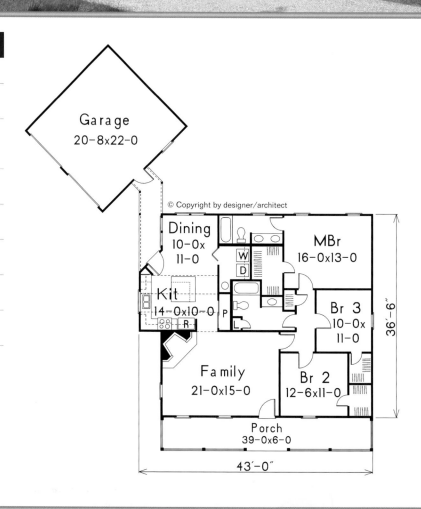

© Copyright by designer/architect

Garage
20-8x22-0

Dining
10-0x
11-0

MBr
16-0x13-0

W
D

Kit
14-0x10-0

Br 3
10-0x
11-0

P

Family
21-0x15-0

Br 2
12-6x11-0

Porch
39-0x6-0

36'-6"

43'-0"

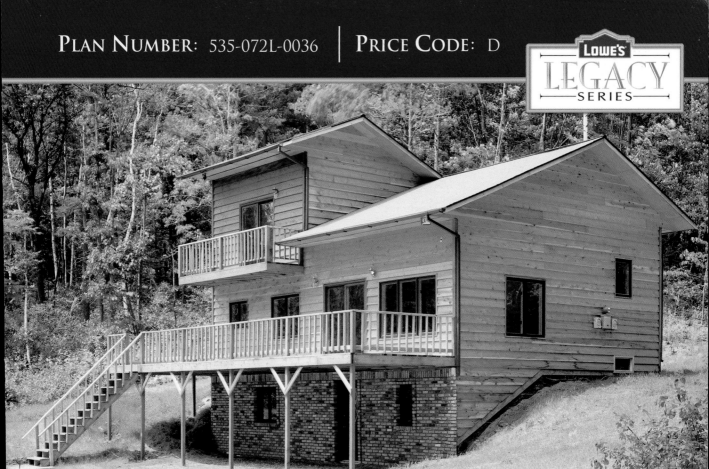

LOWE'S LEGACY SERIES

SPECIAL FEATURES

1,188 total square feet of living area

The large living room with fireplace enjoys a ceiling height of 15' and access to the large deck

The second floor bedroom is a nice escape with its own bath and private deck

A large eating counter in the kitchen creates casual dining space

3 bedrooms, 2 baths, 1-car garage

Walk-out basement foundation

First Floor
936 sq. ft.

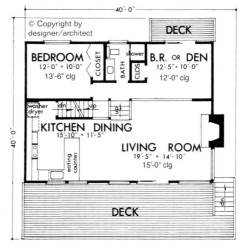

© Copyright by designer/architect

DECK

BEDROOM
12'-0" × 10'-0"
13'-6" clg

B.R. OR DEN
12'-5" × 10'-0"
12'-0" clg

KITCHEN DINING
15'-10" × 11'-5"

LIVING ROOM
19'-5" × 14'-10"
15'-0" clg

eating counter

washer dryer

DECK

Second Floor
252 sq. ft.

BATH

BEDROOM
11'-7" × 11'-5"
10'-0" clg

DECK

Lower Level

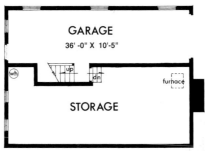

GARAGE
36'-0" X 10'-5"

STORAGE

furnace

SPECIAL FEATURES

2,113 total square feet of living area

Formal living and dining rooms combine to the left of the foyer for an elegant entertaining atmosphere

At the rear of the house, the family room, breakfast area and kitchen flow together for a casual gathering space

All the bedrooms are located on the second floor for extra peace and quiet

4 bedrooms, 2 1/2 baths, 2-car garage

Basement foundation, drawings also include walk-out basement foundation

Second Floor
1,033 sq. ft.

Bedroom #3
10-0 x 12-0

Bedroom #2
10-8 x 12-0

Master Bedroom
15-10 x 14-5

Vaulted Ceiling

DN

Bedroom #4
12-4 x 9-9

Open
To Below

First Floor
1,080 sq. ft.

40'-0"

42'-0"

Deck
12-0 x 12-0

Kitchen
12-0 x 10-4

Brkfst
10-4 x 12-10

Family Room
11-0 x 15-4

R P

Dining Room
12-0 x 11-0

DN

Living Room
12-0 x 11-0

UP Foyer

2-Car Garage
19-5 x 19-4

© Copyright by
designer/architect

SPECIAL FEATURES

1,860 total square feet of living area

Extended counter in the kitchen offers dining space

A bayed breakfast room is open to the great room and kitchen creating a spacious atmosphere

A beautiful corner fireplace in the great room is angled perfectly so it can also be enjoyed by the formal dining room

3 bedrooms, 2 baths, 2-car garage

Basement foundation, drawings also include walk-out basement foundation

Interior View - Great Room

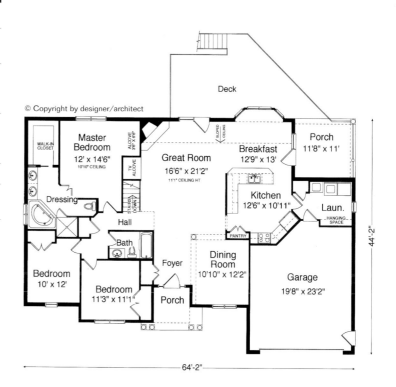

© Copyright by designer/architect

LEGACY SERIES

Special Features

2,143 total square feet of living area

Energy efficient home with
2" x 6" exterior walls

The kitchen handles every task
because of its efficiency

A cozy casual family room has a fireplace
for warmth and a convenient log bin
accessible from the garage as well

Dining and living rooms combine,
perfect for entertaining

4 bedrooms, 3 baths, 2-car garage

Basement foundation

Second Floor
943 sq. ft.

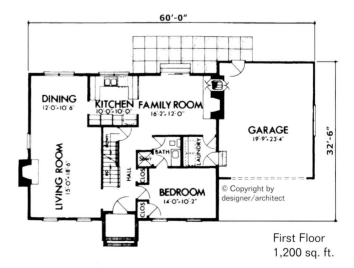

© Copyright by
designer/architect

First Floor
1,200 sq. ft.

SPECIAL FEATURES

1,368 total square feet of living area

Entry foyer steps down to an open living area which combines the great room and formal dining area

Vaulted master bedroom includes a box-bay window and a bath with a large vanity, separate tub and shower

Cozy breakfast area features direct access to the patio and pass-through kitchen

Handy linen closet is located in the hall

3 bedrooms, 2 baths, 2-car garage

Basement foundation

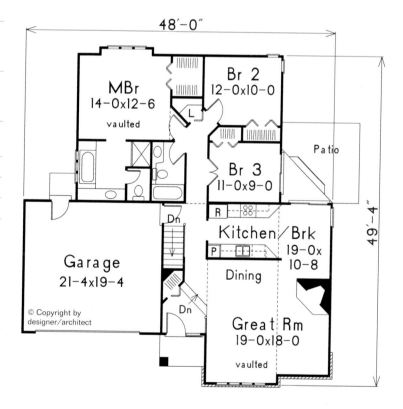

48'-0"

49'-4"

MBr
14-0x12-6
vaulted

Br 2
12-0x10-0

Br 3
11-0x9-0

Patio

Garage
21-4x19-4

Kitchen/Brk
19-0x
10-8

Dining

Great Rm
19-0x18-0
vaulted

Dn

Dn

© Copyright by
designer/architect

SPECIAL FEATURES

1,591 total square feet of living area

Energy efficient home with
2" x 6" exterior walls

Fireplace in great room is accented
by windows on both sides

Practical kitchen is splendidly
designed for organization

Large screen porch is ideal for
three-season entertaining

3 bedrooms, 2 baths, 3-car garage

Basement foundation

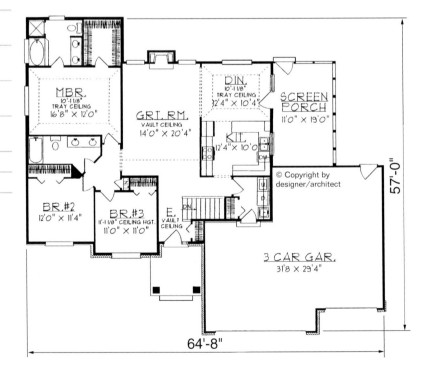

SPECIAL FEATURES

2,082 total square feet of living area

Master bedroom boasts a deluxe bath and a large walk-in closet

Natural light floods the breakfast room through numerous windows

Great room features a 12' ceiling, cozy fireplace and stylish French doors

Bonus room on the second floor has an additional 267 square feet of living area

3 bedrooms, 2 1/2 baths, 2-car garage

Basement foundation

Second Floor
558 sq. ft.

Bedroom
11'1" x 13'3"

Bedroom
11'5" x 12'0"

linen

Bath

bookshelves
computer desk

Balcony   Foyer Below

wood rail

Bonus Room
11'0" x 22'0"

wood rail

60'

Master Bedroom
13'6" x 15'1"

Triple French Doors
w/ arched window above

Great Room
17'4" x 21'2"

12' high ceiling

Dining Room
10'10" x 14'0"

Bath

50'4"

hanging space

walk-in closet

Laun.

Bath

pass thru

Kitchen
12'4" x 11'6"

Foyer

Two-car Garage
22'9" x 22'0"

wood rail

pantry

Breakfast
11' x 9'4"

© Copyright by designer/architect

First Floor
1,524 sq. ft.

SPECIAL FEATURES

2,164 total square feet of living area

Formal and informal spaces create an exceptional family home whether entertaining or relaxing

The master bedroom enjoys a walk-in closet, private bath and the option of a bay window

The second floor loft area is an ideal reading nook

4 bedrooms, 2 1/2 baths, 2-car garage

Basement foundation, drawings also include walk-out basement foundation

FAMILY ROOM
17-4X13-4

OPT. FAMILY RM.

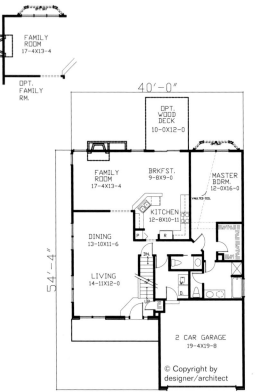

40'-0"

OPT. WOOD DECK
10-0X12-0

54'-4"

FAMILY ROOM
17-4X13-4

BRKFST.
9-8X9-0

MASTER BDRM.
12-0X16-0
VAULTED CEIL.

KITCHEN
12-8X10-11

DINING
13-10X11-6

LIVING
14-11X12-0

DN.

UP.

2 CAR GARAGE
19-4X19-8

© Copyright by designer/architect

First Floor
1,441 sq. ft.

BDRM #3
12-0X13-4

BDRM #2
12-5X10-0

BDRM #4
12-9X11-3

LOFT
11-7X8-9
DN.

OPEN TO BELOW

PLANT LEDGE

VAULTED CEIL.

OPT. DORMER ABOVE

Second Floor
723 sq. ft.

SPECIAL FEATURES

1,602 total square feet of living area

The vaulted living room shines with a two-story window and grand fireplace

Columns define the entry into the formal dining room

A double-door entry adds elegance to the master suite that also enjoys two closets and a private bath

3 bedrooms, 2 1/2 baths, 2-car garage

Basement foundation

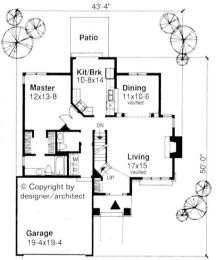

First Floor
1,112 sq. ft.

Second Floor
490 sq. ft.

SPECIAL FEATURES

1,640 total square feet of living area

An open great room and dining area is topped by a stepped ceiling treatment that reaches a 9' height

The functional kitchen enjoys a walk-in pantry, angles and a delightful angled snack bar

Warmth and charm radiate from the corner fireplace through the combined living areas, and a covered porch offers outdoor enjoyment

3 bedrooms, 2 baths, 2-car garage

Basement foundation

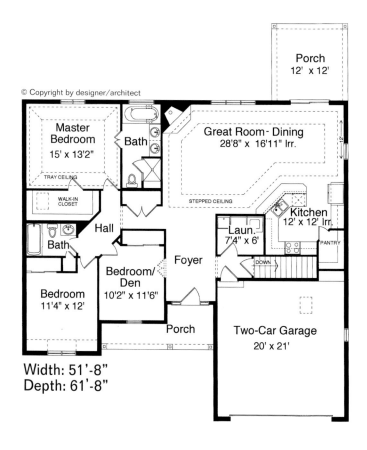

Width: 51'-8"
Depth: 61'-8"

SPECIAL FEATURES

1,359 total square feet of living area

Covered porch, stone chimney and abundant windows lend an outdoor appeal

The spacious and bright kitchen has a pass-through to the formal dining room

Large walk-in closets can be found in all bedrooms

Extensive deck expands dining and entertaining areas

3 bedrooms, 2 1/2 baths, 2-car garage

Basement foundation

Second Floor
691 sq. ft.

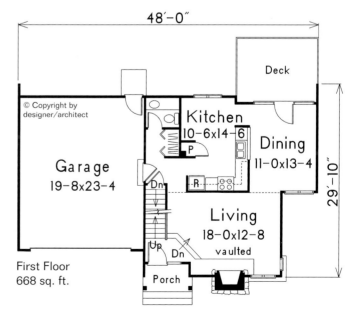

First Floor
668 sq. ft.

SPECIAL FEATURES

1,873 total square feet of living area

Energy efficient home with
2" x 6" exterior walls

This stylish home fits perfectly
on a narrow lot

The vaulted, two-story living room greets
guests and offers a dramatic first impression

The kitchen, bayed dining room and
family room combine for an easy
flow of household activities

3 bedrooms, 2 1/2 baths, 2-car garage

Basement foundation

Second Floor
819 sq. ft.

MBR.
12'8" X 16'0"

BR. #2
12'4" X 11'0"

OPEN TO
LIV.

BR. #3
11'4" X 12'0"

DOWN

PLANT LEDGE

First Floor
1,054 sq. ft.

FAM. RM.
16'8" X 14'0"

DIN.
11'0" X 13'4"

KIT.
11'0" X 11'0"

SHELVES

LIV.
VAULTED CEILING
16'8" X 15'8"

DOWN

2 CAR GAR.
21'8" X 23'4"

E.

44'-0"

44'-0"

© Copyright by
designer/architect

LOWE'S
LEGACY
SERIES

SPECIAL FEATURES

1,317 total square feet of living area

A large window topped by a clerestory window gives the living room a bright, airy feel

A three-way fireplace defines the space between the living and dining rooms

An efficient kitchen neatly serves the dining room

3 bedrooms, 2 baths, 2-car garage

Basement foundation

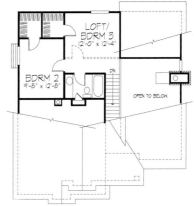

LOFT/
BDRM 3
12'-0" x 12'-4"

BDRM 2
9'-8" x 12'-8"

DN

OPEN TO BELOW

Second Floor
423 sq. ft.

37'-8"

DECK

© Copyright by
designer/architect

MASTER BED.
14'-0" x 12'-4"

KIT
11'-0" x 9'-0"

DINING
10'-0" x 12'-4"
12'-0" clg

DN

38'-8"

CLERESTORY
ABOVE

GARAGE
18'-4" x 18'-4"

LIVING
13'-0" x 15'-8"
17'-0" vaulted clg

First Floor
894 sq. ft.

SPECIAL FEATURES

2,041 total square feet of living area

Great room accesses directly onto the covered rear deck with ceiling fan above

Private master bedroom has a beautiful octagon-shaped sitting area that opens and brightens the space

Two secondary bedrooms share a full bath

3 bedrooms, 2 baths, 2-car side entry garage

Walk-out basement foundation

Interior View - Lower Level

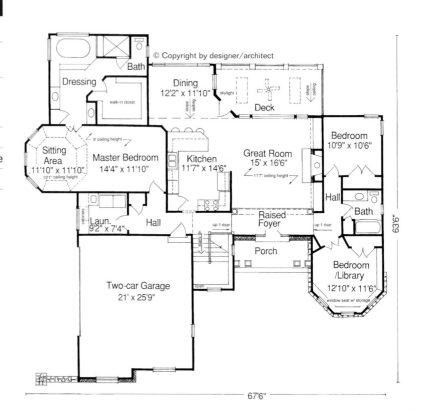

© Copyright by designer/architect

Bath

Dressing

walk-in closet

9' ceiling height

Sitting Area
11'10" x 11'10"
10'1" ceiling height

Master Bedroom
14'4" x 11'10"

Kitchen
11'7" x 14'6"

Dining
12'2" x 11'10"

skylight

slope ceiling

slope ceiling

Deck

Bedroom
10'9" x 10'6"

Great Room
15' x 16'6"
11'7" ceiling height

Hall

Bath

cabinets

Laun.
9'2" x 7'4"

Hall

up 1 riser

Raised Foyer

up 1 riser

Two-car Garage
21' x 25'9"

open

stairs down

Porch

Bedroom
/Library
12'10" x 11'6"

window seat w/ storage

636"

67'6"

SPECIAL FEATURES

1,268 total square feet of living area

Multiple gables, large porch and arched windows create a classy exterior

Innovative design provides openness in the great room, kitchen and breakfast room

Secondary bedrooms have private hall with bath

2" x 6" exterior walls available, please order plan #535-007E-0060

3 bedrooms, 2 baths, 2-car garage

Basement foundation, drawings also include crawl space and slab foundations

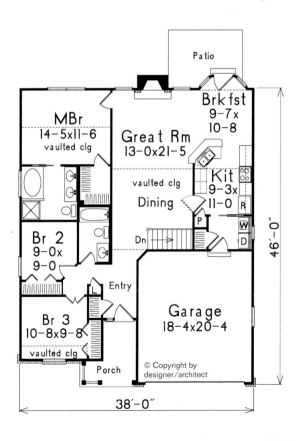

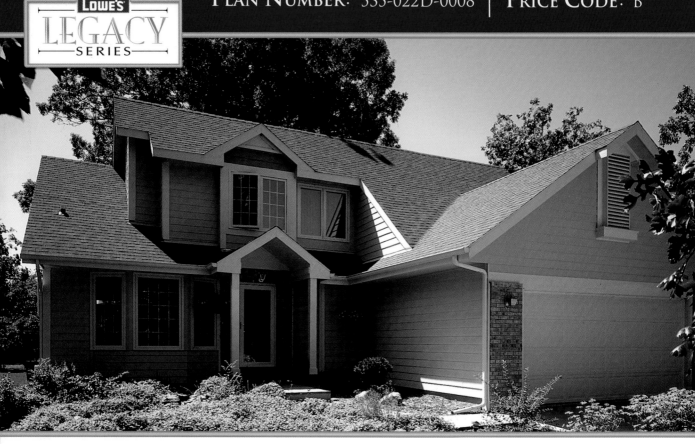

SPECIAL FEATURES

1,565 total square feet of living area

Highly-detailed exterior adds value

Large vaulted great room with a full wall of glass opens onto the corner deck

Loft/bedroom #3 opens to rooms below and adds to the spacious feeling

Bay-windowed kitchen with a cozy morning room

Master bath features a platform tub, separate shower and a large walk-in closet

3 bedrooms, 2 1/2 baths, 2-car garage

Basement foundation

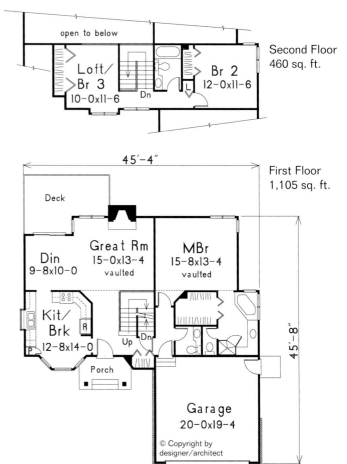

Second Floor
460 sq. ft.

First Floor
1,105 sq. ft.

© Copyright by designer/architect

SPECIAL FEATURES

1,739 total square feet of living area

The secluded kitchen is a chef's dream and stays bright with corner windows

The oversized living room includes space for an optional fireplace and enjoys sliding glass doors leading to the rear deck

The master bedroom features a private vanity and tub while sharing the first floor half bath

3 bedrooms, 2 baths, 2-car garage

Basement foundation

Second Floor
550 sq. ft.

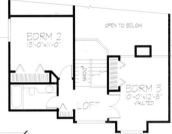

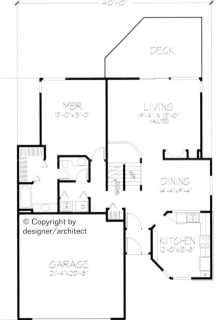

First Floor
1,189 sq. ft.

© Copyright by designer/architect

SPECIAL FEATURES

1,666 total square feet of living area

Energy efficient home with
2" x 6" exterior walls

Airy living room features a
10' ceiling and grand fireplace

A walk-in closet and deluxe bath with
whirlpool tub grace the master bedroom

Kitchen and dining room combine
for an open gathering area

Secondary bedrooms share
a compartmented bath

3 bedrooms, 2 1/2 baths, 2-car garage

Basement foundation

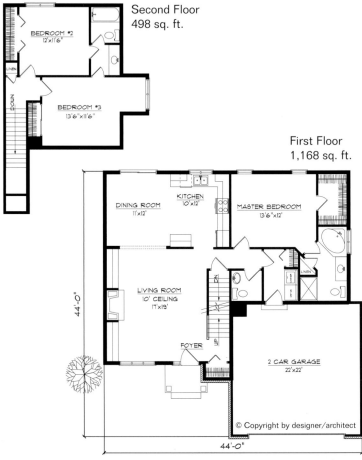

Second Floor
498 sq. ft.

First Floor
1,168 sq. ft.

© Copyright by designer/architect

SPECIAL FEATURES

1,721 total square feet of living area

Roof dormers add great curb appeal

Vaulted dining and great rooms
are immersed in light from
the atrium window wall

Functionally designed kitchen

2" x 6" exterior walls available,
please order plan #535-007E-0010

1,604 square feet on the first floor and
117 square feet on the lower level atrium

3 bedrooms, 2 baths, 3-car garage

Walk-out basement foundation,
drawings also include crawl
space and slab foundations

Rear View

LOWE'S
LEGACY
SERIES

SPECIAL FEATURES

1,767 total square feet of living area

Vaulted dining room has a
view onto the patio

Master suite is vaulted with a
private bath and walk-in closet

An arched entry leads to the vaulted living
room featuring tall windows and a fireplace

3 bedrooms, 2 1/2 baths, 2-car garage

Basement foundation

Interior View - Living Room

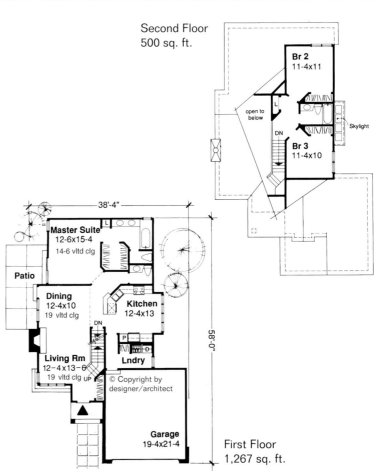

Second Floor
500 sq. ft.

Br 2
11-4x11

open to
below

L

DN

Skylight

Br 3
11-4x10

38'-4"

Master Suite
12-6x15-4
14-6 vltd clg

Patio

Dining
12-4x10
19 vltd clg

Kitchen
12-4x13

58'-0"

DN

Living Rm
12-4x13-6
19 vltd clg UP

Lndry

P

© Copyright by
designer/architect

Garage
19-4x21-4

First Floor
1,267 sq. ft.

LOWE'S
LEGACY
SERIES

SPECIAL FEATURES

1,558 total square feet of living area

Energy efficient home with
2" x 6" exterior walls

The spacious utility room is located
conveniently between the garage
and kitchen/dining area

Bedrooms are separated from
the living area by a hallway

Enormous living area with fireplace
and vaulted ceiling opens to the
kitchen and dining area

Master bedroom is enhanced with a large
bay window, walk-in closet and private bath

3 bedrooms, 2 baths, 2-car garage

Basement foundation

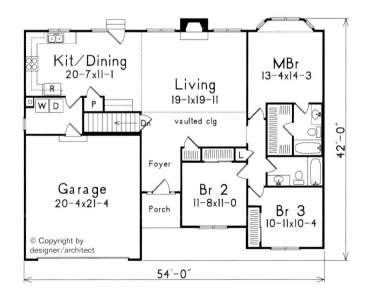

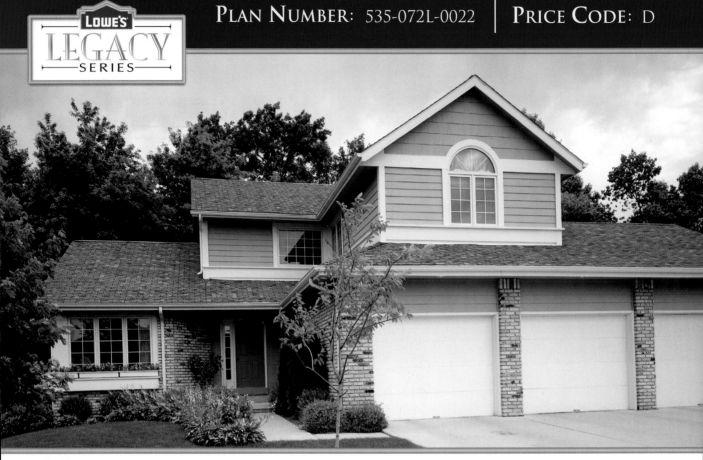

SPECIAL FEATURES

1,891 total square feet of living area

Step down into the combined dining and great rooms topped with a vaulted ceiling

A bay window highlights the family room

Three bedrooms enjoy the privacy of the second floor

3 bedrooms, 2 1/2 baths, 2-car garage

Basement foundation

Second Floor
816 sq. ft.

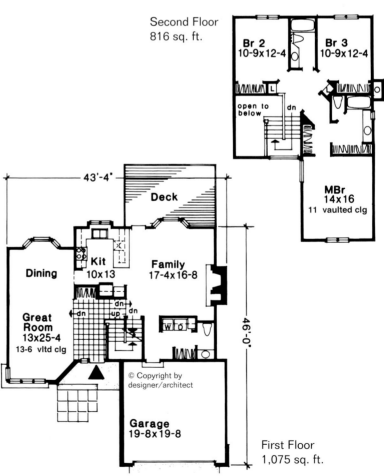

First Floor
1,075 sq. ft.

© Copyright by designer/architect

SPECIAL FEATURES

1,516 total square feet of living area

All living and dining areas are interconnected for a spacious look and easy movement

Covered entrance leads into the sunken great room with a rugged corner fireplace

Family kitchen combines practicality with access to other areas

Second floor loft opens to rooms below and can convert to a third bedroom

The dormer in bedroom #2 adds interest

2 bedrooms, 2 1/2 baths, 2-car garage

Basement foundation

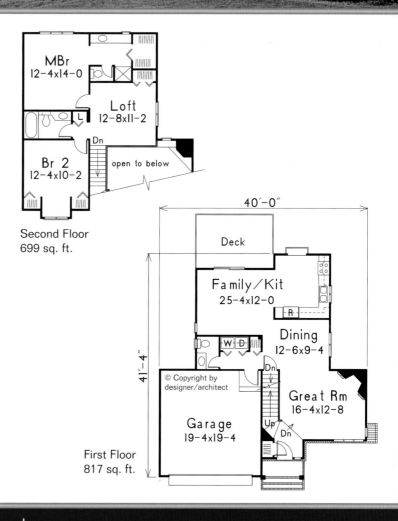

Second Floor
699 sq. ft.

MBr
12-4x14-0

Loft
12-8x11-2

Dn

Br 2
12-4x10-2

open to below

40'-0"

Deck

Family/Kit
25-4x12-0

Dining
12-6x9-4

41'-4"

© Copyright by designer/architect

W D

Dn

Great Rm
16-4x12-8

Garage
19-4x19-4

Up

Dn

First Floor
817 sq. ft.

SPECIAL FEATURES

1,820 total square feet of living area

A bay window and cozy fireplace create enticing surroundings in the casual family room

Decorative columns are pleasing to the eye and separate the dining and living rooms while maintaining an open feeling

An 11'-6" vaulted ceiling creates an airy interior in the master suite

4 bedrooms, 2 1/2 baths, 3-car garage

Basement foundation

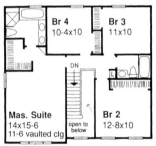

Second Floor
833 sq. ft.

Br 4
10-4x10

Br 3
11x10

DN

Mas. Suite
14x15-6
11-6 vaulted clg

open to below

Br 2
12-8x10

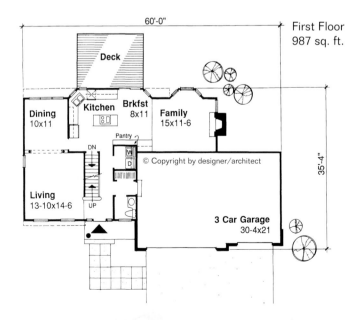

First Floor
987 sq. ft.

60'-0"

Deck

Dining
10x11

Kitchen

Brkfst
8x11

Family
15x11-6

Pantry

DN

W D

© Copyright by designer/architect

Living
13-10x14-6

UP

35'-4"

3 Car Garage
30-4x21

SPECIAL FEATURES

- 2,101 total square feet of living area
- Sunken great room has balcony above
- Octagon-shaped master bedroom is private
- Luxurious amenities in a modest size
- 3 bedrooms, 2 1/2 baths, 2-car garage
- Basement foundation

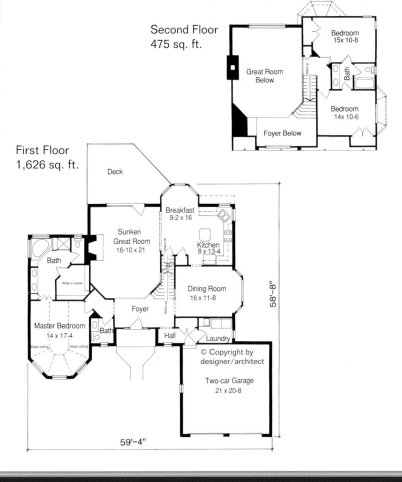

Second Floor
475 sq. ft.

Great Room Below

Bedroom
15 x 10-8

Bath

Bedroom
14x 10-6

Foyer Below

First Floor
1,626 sq. ft.

Deck

Breakfast
9-2 x 16

Sunken Great Room
16-10 x 21

Kitchen
8 x 13-4

Bath

Walk-in closet

Dining Room
16 x 11-8

Master Bedroom
14 x 17-4

Foyer

Bath

Hall

Laundry

Slope ceiling

© Copyright by designer/architect

Two-car Garage
21 x 20-8

58'-8"

59'-4"

SPECIAL FEATURES

1,444 total square feet of living area

11' ceilings in the living and dining rooms combine with a central fireplace to create a large open living area

Both secondary bedrooms have large walk-in closets

Extra space in the garage is suitable for a workshop or play area

Front and rear covered porches add a cozy touch

U-shaped kitchen includes a laundry closet and serving bar

3 bedrooms, 2 baths, 2-car side entry garage

Slab foundation, drawings also include crawl space foundation

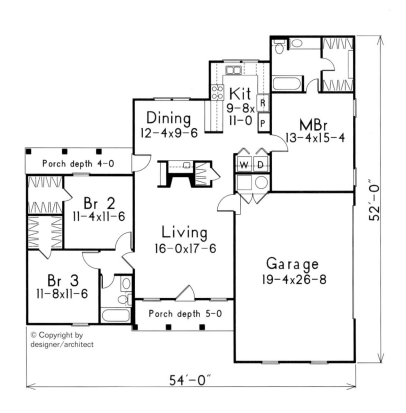

SPECIAL FEATURES

2,029 total square feet of living area

Stonework, gables, roof dormer and double porches create a country flavor

Kitchen enjoys extravagant cabinetry and counterspace in a bay, island snack bar, built-in pantry and cheery dining area with multiple tall windows

Angled stair descends from large entry with wood columns and is open to a vaulted great room with corner fireplace

Master bedroom boasts two walk-in closets, a private bath with double-door entry and a secluded porch

2" x 6" exterior walls available, please order plan #535-007E-0055

4 bedrooms, 2 baths, 2-car side entry garage

Basement foundation, drawings also include crawl space and slab foundations

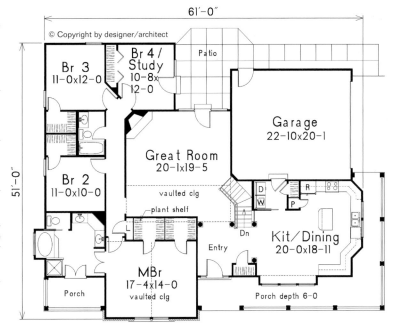

© Copyright by designer/architect

61'-0"

51'-0"

Br 3
11-0x12-0

Br 4 /
Study
10-8x
12-0

Patio

Garage
22-10x20-1

Br 2
11-0x10-0

Great Room
20-1x19-5
vaulted clg

plant shelf

Kit/Dining
20-0x18-11

MBr
17-4x14-0
vaulted clg

Entry

Porch

Porch depth 6-0

SPECIAL FEATURES

2,041 total square feet of living area

Energy efficient home with
2" x 6" exterior walls

Wonderful sunken family room features
a fireplace and accesses the patio

The kitchen with island cooktop
and nook combines with the family
room creating an open area

Dining room is accessible from the
kitchen and vaulted living room

Bedroom #4 could easily
convert to a study or den

4 bedrooms, 3 baths, 2-car side entry garage

Partial basement/slab foundation

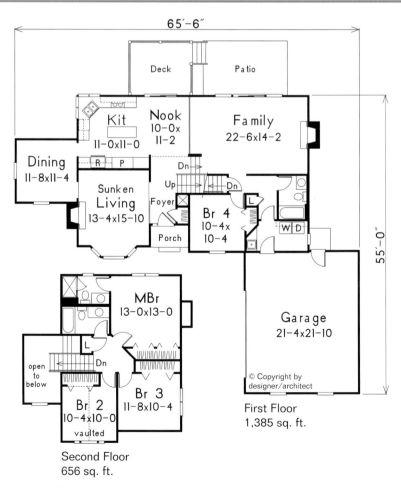

First Floor
1,385 sq. ft.

Second Floor
656 sq. ft.

LOWE'S LEGACY SERIES

SPECIAL FEATURES

1,668 total square feet of living area

Large bay windows grace the breakfast area, master bedroom and dining room

Extensive walk-in closets and storage spaces are located throughout the home

Handy covered entry porch

Large living room has a fireplace, built-in bookshelves and a sloped ceiling

3 bedrooms, 2 baths, 2-car drive under garage

Basement foundation

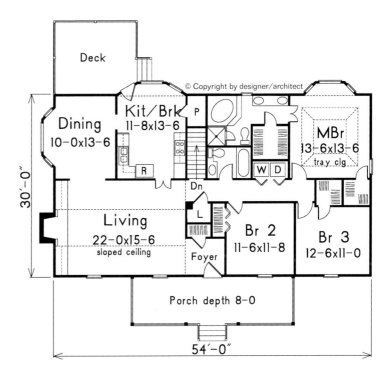

Deck

© Copyright by designer/architect

Kit/Brk 11-8x13-6

P

Dining 10-0x13-6

R

MBr 13-6x13-6 tray clg

W   D

Dn

Living 22-0x15-6 sloped ceiling

L

Br 2 11-6x11-8

Br 3 12-6x11-0

Foyer

30'-0"

Porch depth 8-0

54'-0"

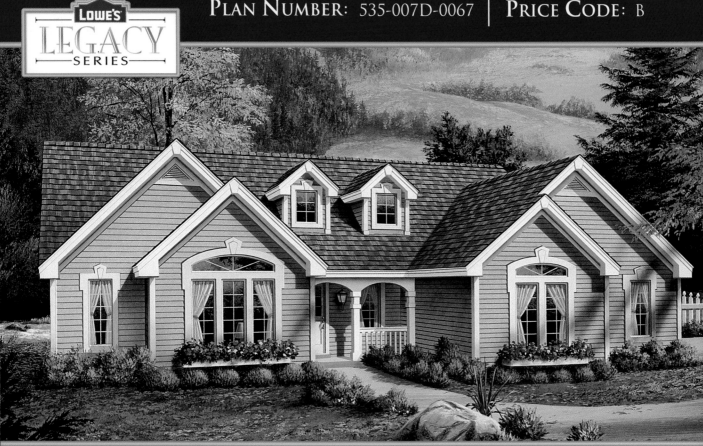

SPECIAL FEATURES

1,761 total square feet of living area

Exterior window dressing, roof dormers and planter boxes provide visual warmth and charm

Great room boasts a vaulted ceiling, fireplace and opens to a pass-through kitchen

The vaulted master bedroom includes a luxury bath and walk-in closet

Home features eight separate closets with an abundance of storage

4 bedrooms, 2 baths, 2-car side entry garage

Basement foundation

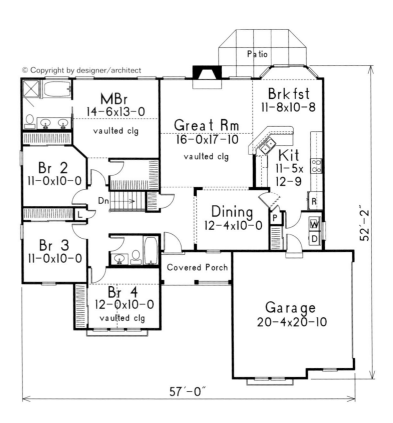

© Copyright by designer/architect

Patio

MBr
14-6x13-0
vaulted clg

Great Rm
16-0x17-10
vaulted clg

Brkfst
11-8x10-8

Kit
11-5x
12-9

Br 2
11-0x10-0

Dn

Dining
12-4x10-0

Br 3
11-0x10-0

Covered Porch

Br 4
12-0x10-0
vaulted clg

Garage
20-4x20-10

52'-2"

57'-0"

SPECIAL FEATURES

1,728 total square feet of living area

Large entry leads to the family room featuring a corner fireplace and a window wall overlooking an enormous deck

Master bedroom is adorned with a dramatic bath featuring an angled entry and a corner tub

Design also includes a detached garage option

3 bedrooms, 2 baths, 3-car drive under garage

Basement foundation, drawings also include crawl space foundation

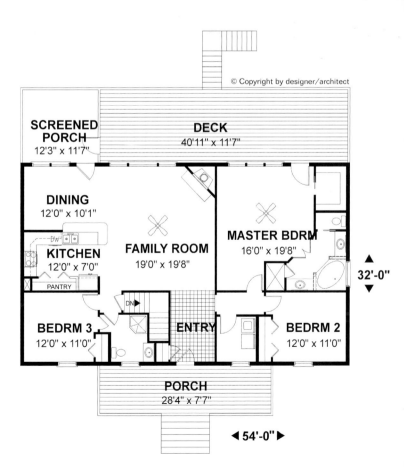

© Copyright by designer/architect

SCREENED PORCH
12'3" x 11'7"

DECK
40'11" x 11'7"

DINING
12'0" x 10'1"

FAMILY ROOM
19'0" x 19'8"

MASTER BDRM
16'0" x 19'8"

KITCHEN
12'0" x 7'0"

PANTRY

DW

DN ►

BEDRM 3
12'0" x 11'0"

ENTRY

BEDRM 2
12'0" x 11'0"

PORCH
28'4" x 7'7"

32'-0"

◄ 54'-0" ►

SERIES

SPECIAL FEATURES

1,360 total square feet of living area

Kitchen/dining room features an island workspace and plenty of dining area

Master bedroom has a large walk-in closet and private bath

Laundry room is adjacent to the kitchen for easy access

Convenient workshop in garage

Large closets in secondary bedrooms maintain organization

3 bedrooms, 2 baths, 2-car side entry garage

Basement foundation, drawings also include crawl space and slab foundations

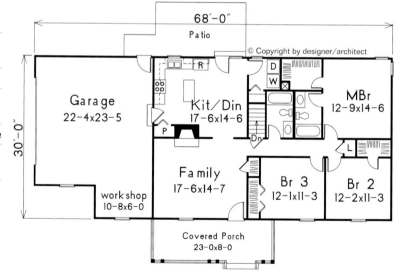

68'-0"

Patio

© Copyright by designer/architect

30'-0"

Garage
22-4x23-5

Kit/Din
17-6x14-6

MBr
12-9x14-6

workshop
10-8x6-0

Family
17-6x14-7

Br 3
12-1x11-3

Br 2
12-2x11-3

Covered Porch
23-0x8-0

SERIES

SPECIAL FEATURES

1,835 total square feet of living area

The arched entry and vaulted foyer create a welcoming appearance

Divided dining and living rooms continue with vaulted ceilings to provide a distinguished openness

Country kitchen with cozy fireplace and greenhouse windows offers a central gathering area

Open stairway overlooks foyer

All bedrooms are located on the second floor for added privacy

3 bedrooms, 2 1/2 baths, 2-car garage

Basement foundation

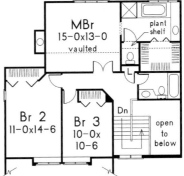

Second Floor
907 sq. ft.

MBr
15-0x13-0
vaulted

plant shelf

Br 2
11-0x14-6

Br 3
10-0x
10-6

Dn

open
to
below

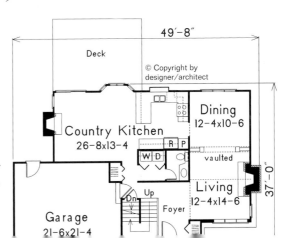

First Floor
928 sq. ft.

49'-8"

Deck

© Copyright by
designer/architect

Country Kitchen
26-8x13-4

Dining
12-4x10-6

vaulted

W D

R P

Living
12-4x14-6

37'-0"

Up

Dn

Foyer

Garage
21-6x21-4

SPECIAL FEATURES

1,128 total square feet of living area

Large living room borrows from dining area creating an expansive space

Well-arranged U-shaped kitchen has lots of counter and cabinet storage space

Double closets and a full bath accompany the spacious master bedroom

Oversized garage with ample storage has a door to the rear patio that leads to the dining area

2 bedrooms, 2 baths, 2-car garage

Basement foundation

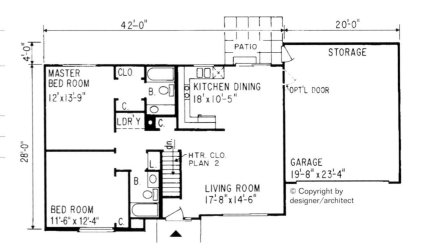

© Copyright by designer/architect

LOWE'S
LEGACY
SERIES

SPECIAL FEATURES

1,791 total square feet of living area

Vaulted great room and octagon-shaped dining area enjoy a spectacular view of the covered patio

Kitchen features a pass-through to the dining area, center island, large walk-in pantry and breakfast room with large bay window

The master bedroom enjoys a vaulted ceiling and a sitting area

The garage includes extra storage space

2" x 6" exterior walls available, please order plan #535-007E-0049

4 bedrooms, 2 baths, 2-car garage

Basement foundation, drawings also include crawl space and slab foundations

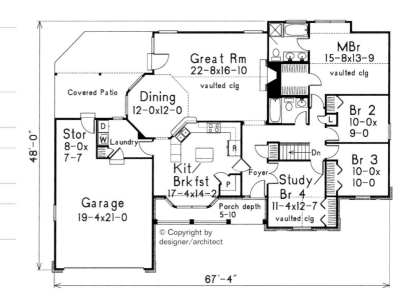

SPECIAL FEATURES

1,508 total square feet of living area

Energy efficient home with
2" x 6" exterior walls

The kitchen counter wraps around
to the dining room which features
access to the outdoors

The master bedroom is a relaxing retreat
with a walk-in closet and private bath

3 bedrooms, 2 baths, 2-car garage

Basement foundation

© Copyright by designer/architect

SPECIAL FEATURES

1,501 total square feet of living area

Spacious kitchen with dining area is open to the outdoors

Convenient utility room is adjacent to the garage

Master bedroom features a private bath, dressing area and access to the large covered porch

Large family room creates openness

3 bedrooms, 2 baths, 2-car side entry garage

Basement foundation, drawings also include crawl space and slab foundations

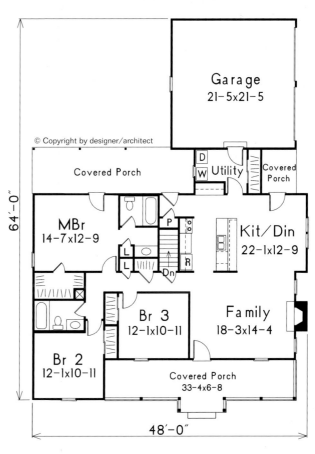

© Copyright by designer/architect

Garage
21-5x21-5

Covered Porch

Utility

Covered Porch

MBr
14-7x12-9

Kit/Din
22-1x12-9

64'-0"

Br 3
12-1x10-11

Family
18-3x14-4

Br 2
12-1x10-11

Covered Porch
33-4x6-8

48'-0"

SPECIAL FEATURES

1,384 total square feet of living area

Wrap-around country porch
for peaceful evenings

Vaulted great room enjoys a large
bay window, stone fireplace, pass-
through kitchen and awesome rear
views through an atrium window wall

Master bedroom features a double-door
entry, walk-in closet and a fabulous bath

Atrium opens to 611 square feet
of optional living area below

2 bedrooms, 2 baths, 1-car side entry garage

Walk-out basement foundation

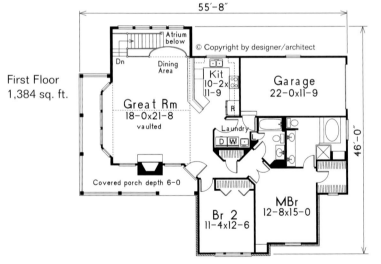

First Floor
1,384 sq. ft.

55'-8"

46'-0"

© Copyright by designer/architect

Atrium below

Dn

Dining Area

Kit
10-2x
11-9

Garage
22-0x11-9

R

Great Rm
18-0x21-8
vaulted

Laundry

D W

Covered porch depth 6-0

MBr
12-8x15-0

Br 2
11-4x12-6

Rear View

Optional
Lower Level

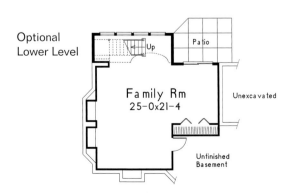

Up

Patio

Family Rm
25-0x21-4

Unexcavated

Unfinished
Basement

SPECIAL FEATURES

1,209 total square feet of living area

Bracketed shed roof and ski storage add charm to this vacation home

The living room enjoys a sloped ceiling, second floor balcony overlook and view to a large deck

Kitchen features a snack bar and access to the second floor via a circular staircase

Second floor includes two bedrooms with sizable closets, center hall bath and balcony overlooking rooms below

3 bedrooms, 2 baths

Crawl space foundation

First Floor
780 sq. ft.

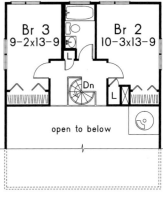

Second Floor
429 sq. ft.

SPECIAL FEATURES

1,727 total square feet of living area

This home is designed with an insulated foundation system featuring pre-mounted insulation on concrete walls providing a drier, warmer and smarter structure

The breakfast bay with access onto the covered porch is a bright and cheery place to start the day

A furniture alcove adds space to the formal dining room

A rear entry hall offers storage closets and a large laundry room

All bedrooms are located on the second floor for extra privacy

3 bedrooms, 2 1/2 baths, 2-car garage

Basement foundation

Second Floor
786 sq. ft.

First Floor
941 sq. ft.

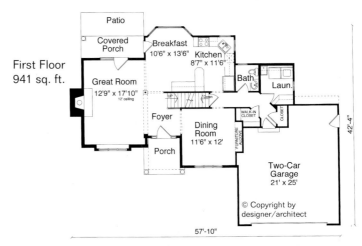

© Copyright by designer/architect

SPECIAL FEATURES

1,992 total square feet of living area

Interesting angled walls add drama to many of the living areas including the family room, master bedroom and breakfast area

Covered porch includes a spa and an outdoor kitchen with sink, refrigerator and cooktop

Enter the majestic master bath to find a dramatic corner oversized tub

4 bedrooms, 3 baths, 2-car side entry garage

Basement foundation, drawings also include crawl space and slab foundations

Rear View

BONUS ROOM
10'-7" x 22'-6"

GARAGE
22'-0" x 22'-6"

DECK
24'-8" x 15'-5"

COVERED PORCH
24'-10" x 12'-0"

HIS

SINK
REFRIG
COOKTOP

6' SPA

MECH.

OPTIONAL STAIRS TO BASEMENT

TV NICHE ABOVE
VENTLESS GAS FIREPLACE

SHOWER

SEAT

TRAY CEILING

SITTING

CLERESTORY WINDOW ABOVE

BREAKFAST
8'-6" x 11'-0"

HERS

MASTER BEDROOM
19'-0" x 15'-0"

19'-9" HIGH CEILING

KITCHEN
17'-3" x 12'-6"

PANT.

DW

FAMILY ROOM
16'-0" x 21'-10"

OPTIONAL OPENING FOR LIVING

LINE OF 9' HIGH CEILING

BEDROOM 2
11'-0" x 14'-0"

LIVING / BEDROOM 3
11'-0" x 12'-0"

OPEN TO DORMER ABOVE

DINING
13'-8" x 12'-0"

MEDIA / GUEST ROOM
13'-8" x 11'-0"

PORCH
33'-4" x 6'-0"

© Copyright by designer/architect

62'-0"

66'-2"

SPECIAL FEATURES

2,067 total square feet of living area

An enormous master bath has separate vanities, a whirlpool tub and a walk-in closet on each end

The flex space would make an excellent formal dining room or home office space

The rear covered porch is a fantastic outdoor retreat and leads onto the open patio

The unfinished bonus room has an additional 379 square feet of living area

3 bedrooms, 2 1/2 baths, 2-car garage

Slab foundation, drawings also include crawl space foundation

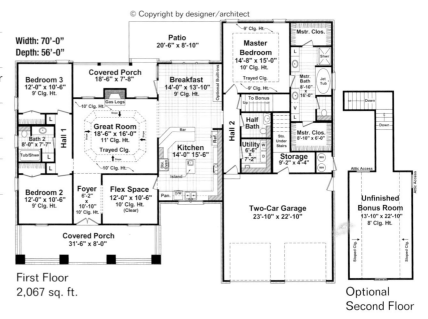

© Copyright by designer/architect

Width: 70'-0"
Depth: 56'-0"

Patio
20'-6" x 8'-10"

Covered Porch
18'-6" x 7'-8"

Bedroom 3
12'-0" x 10'-6"
9' Clg. Ht.

Gas Logs

Great Room
18'-6" x 16'-0"
11' Clg. Ht.
Trayed Clg.

10' Clg. Ht.

Bath 2
8'-0" x 7'-7"

Hall 1

Breakfast
14'-0" x 13'-10"
9' Clg. Ht.

Optional Built-ins

9' Clg. Ht.

Master Bedroom
14'-8" x 15'-0"
10' Clg. Ht.
Trayed Clg.

Mstr. Clos.

Mstr. Bath
8'-10" x 16'-0"

To Bonus Up

Half Bath

Hall 2

Kitchen
14'-0" 15'-6"

Bar

Ref.

Sto. Under Stairs

Mstr. Clos.
8'-10" x 6'-0"

Utility
6'-6" x 7'-2"

Storage
9'-2" x 4'-4"

Tub/Shwr

Bedroom 2
12'-0" x 10'-6"
9' Clg. Ht.

Foyer
6'-2" x 10'-10"

Flex Space
12'-0" x 10'-6"
10' Clg. Ht.
(Clear)

Island

Pan.

D/W

Dbl. Oven

Covered Porch
31'-6" x 8'-0"

Two-Car Garage
23'-10" x 22'-10"

First Floor
2,067 sq. ft.

Attic Access

Attic Access

Down

Down

Unfinished Bonus Room
13'-10" x 22'-10"
8' Clg. Ht.

Sloped Clg.

Sloped Clg.

Optional Second Floor

SPECIAL FEATURES

1,977 total square feet of living area

Classic traditional exterior is always in style

Spacious great room boasts a vaulted ceiling, dining area, atrium with elegant staircase and feature windows

Atrium opens to 1,416 square feet of optional living area below which consists of a family room, two bedrooms, two baths and a study

2" x 6" exterior walls available, please order plan #535-007E-0077

4 bedrooms, 2 1/2 baths, 3-car side entry garage

Walk-out basement foundation

76'-0"

45'-0"

MBr 14-6x15-5

Br 2 10-7x 10-0

Br 3 11-4x11x8

Br 4 11-8x12-8 vaulted

open to below   Dn

Brk 11-8x13-0

Deck

Great Rm 16-4x24-2 vaulted

Kit 11-3x 12-4

Dining

Porch

Garage 23-4x29-4

© Copyright by designer/architect

First Floor 1,977 sq. ft.

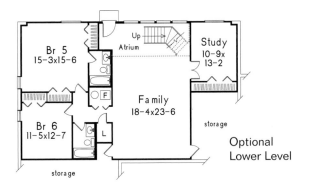

Br 5 15-3x15-6

Up

Atrium

Study 10-9x 13-2

Family 18-4x23-6

Br 6 11-5x12-7

storage

storage

Optional Lower Level

LOWE'S LEGACY SERIES

SPECIAL FEATURES

1,339 total square feet of living area

Full-length covered porch enhances front facade

Vaulted ceiling and stone fireplace add drama to the family room

Walk-in closets in the bedrooms provide ample storage space

Combined kitchen/dining area adjoins the family room for the perfect entertaining space

2" x 6" exterior walls available, please order plan #535-058D-0072

3 bedrooms, 2 1/2 baths

Crawl space foundation

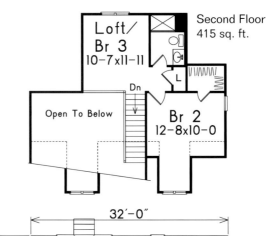

Second Floor
415 sq. ft.

Loft/Br 3
10-7x11-11

Br 2
12-8x10-0

Open To Below

Dn

L

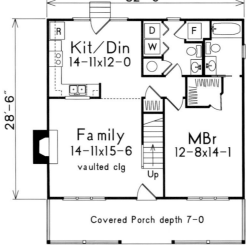

First Floor
924 sq. ft.

32'-0"

28'-6"

Kit/Din
14-11x12-0

Family
14-11x15-6
vaulted clg

MBr
12-8x14-1

R D W F

Up

Covered Porch depth 7-0

© Copyright by designer/architect

SPECIAL FEATURES

1,584 total square feet of living area

Vaulted living and dining rooms feature a stone fireplace, descending spiral staircase and a separate vestibule with guest closet

Space-saving kitchen has an eat-in area and access to the deck

Bedroom #1 has private access to a full bath

3 bedrooms, 2 baths

Partial basement/crawl space foundation, drawings also include crawl space foundation

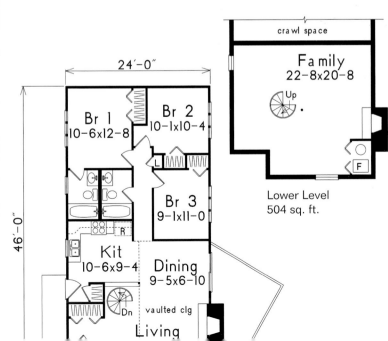

24'-0"

Br 1
10-6x12-8

Br 2
10-1x10-4

Br 3
9-1x11-0

46'-0"

Kit
10-6x9-4

Dining
9-5x6-10

R

L

Dn

vaulted clg

Living

crawl space

Family
22-8x20-8

Up

F

Lower Level
504 sq. ft.

PLAN NUMBER: 535-057D-0034 | PRICE CODE: AAA

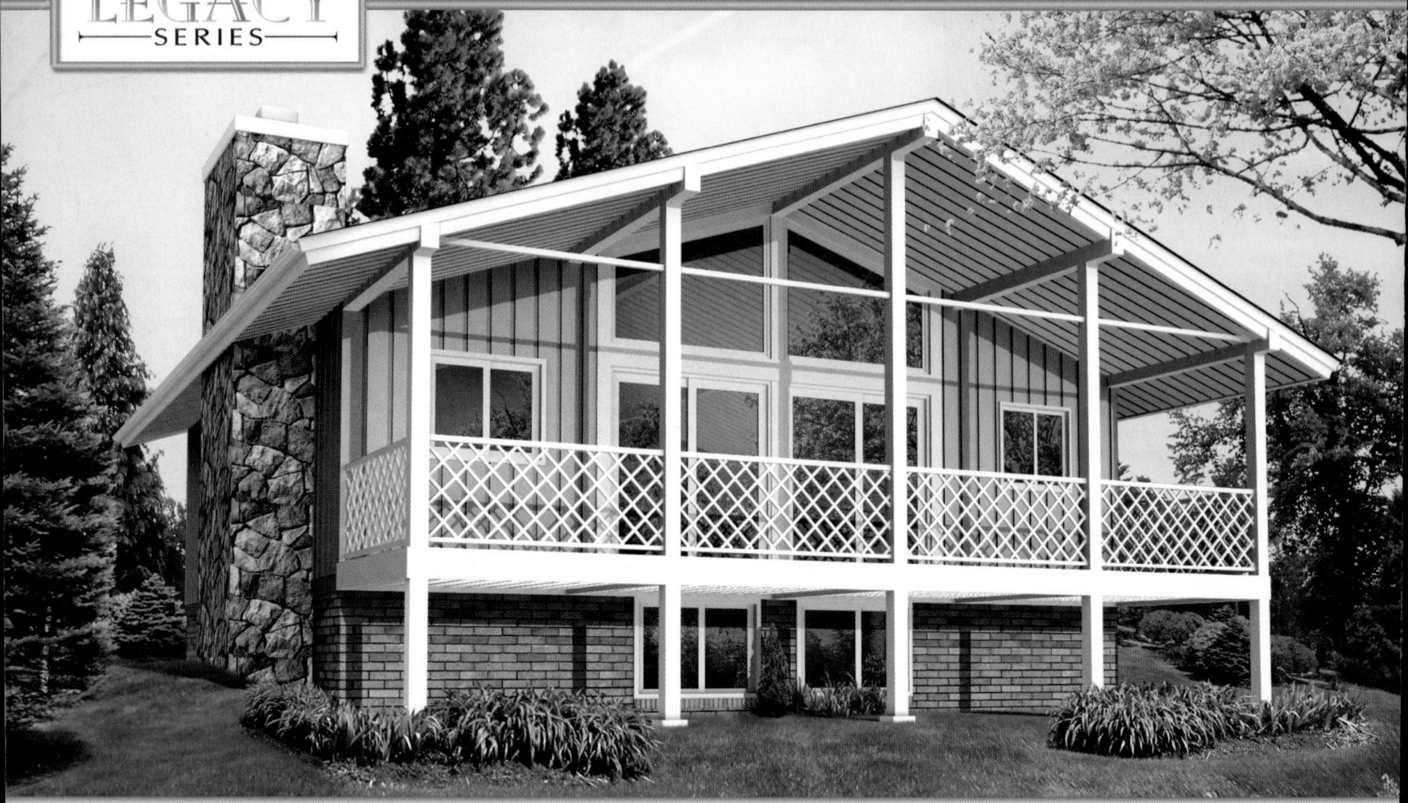

SPECIAL FEATURES

- 1,020 total square feet of living area
- The extra-wide porch offers an enchanting atmosphere to take in the surrounding views
- Inside, the expansive living/dining area is completely open to the kitchen for ideal entertaining
- The master bedroom conveniently houses two closets
- 2 bedrooms, 1 bath
- Basement foundation

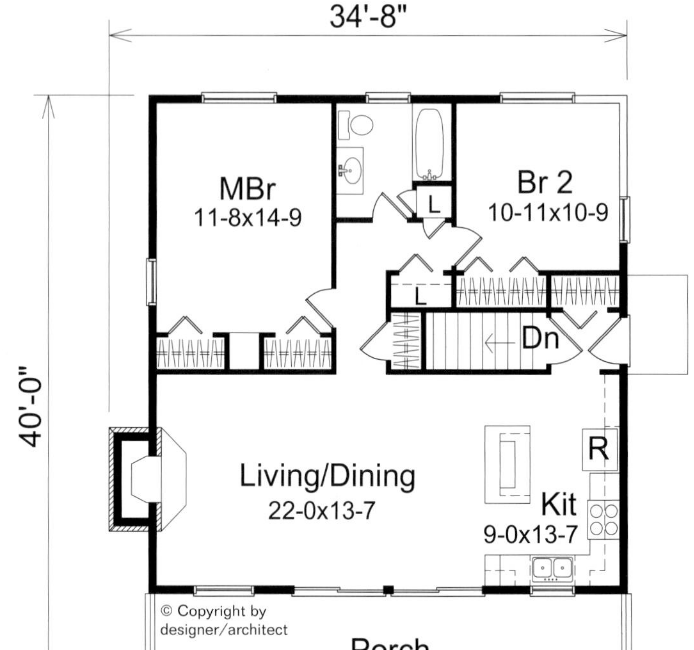

34'-8"
40'-0"
MBr
11-8x14-9
Br 2
10-11x10-9
L
L
Dn
R
Living/Dining
22-0x13-7
Kit
9-0x13-7
© Copyright by
designer/architect
Porch
32-0x8-0

SPECIAL FEATURES

1,684 total square feet of living area

Delightful wrap-around porch is anchored by a full masonry fireplace

The vaulted great room includes a large bay window, fireplace, dining balcony and atrium window wall

Double walk-in closets, large luxury bath and sliding doors to an exterior balcony are a few fantastic features of the master bedroom

Atrium opens to 611 square feet of optional living area on the lower level

3 bedrooms, 2 baths, 2-car drive under rear entry garage

Walk-out basement foundation

Rear View

First Floor
1,684 sq. ft.

© Copyright by designer/architect

Optional Lower Level

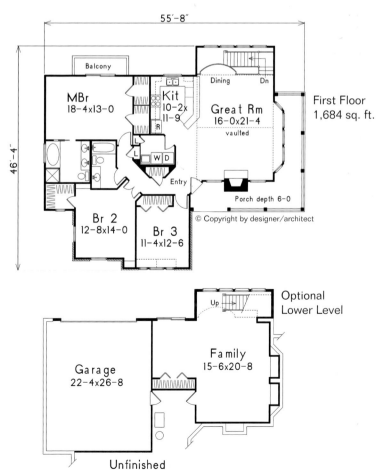

Unfinished

Lowe's LEGACY SERIES

SPECIAL FEATURES

1,657 total square feet of living area

The kitchen features a stylish pass-through to the living room

Master bedroom is secluded from the living area for privacy

Large windows in the breakfast and dining areas create a bright and cheerful atmosphere

3 bedrooms, 2 1/2 baths, 2-car drive under garage

Basement foundation

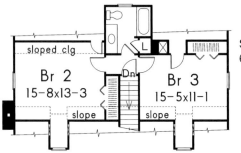

Second Floor
611 sq. ft.

sloped clg

Br 2
15-8x13-3

Dn

Br 3
15-5x11-1

slope   slope

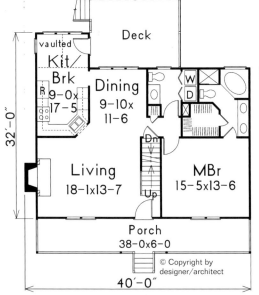

First Floor
1,046 sq. ft.

Deck

vaulted

Kit/
Brk
9-0x
17-5

Dining
9-10x
11-6

W
D

Dn

Living
18-1x13-7

MBr
15-5x13-6

Up

32'-0"

Porch
38-0x6-0

© Copyright by
designer/architect

40'-0"

SPECIAL FEATURES

1,855 total square feet of living area

Angled stairs add character
to the two-story foyer

Secluded dining area is formal and elegant

Sunny master bedroom has all the luxuries

A half bath is conveniently located
off the kitchen and breakfast area

3 bedrooms, 2 1/2 baths, 2-car garage

Basement foundation

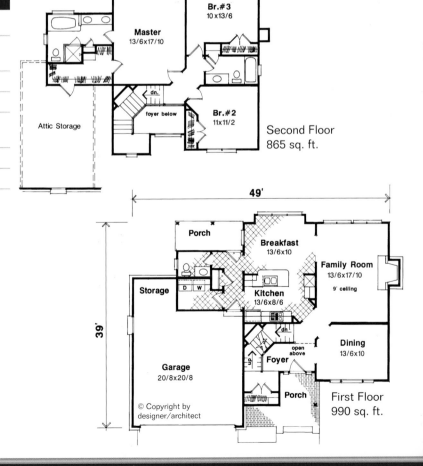

Second Floor
865 sq. ft.

First Floor
990 sq. ft.

© Copyright by
designer/architect

SPECIAL FEATURES

1,140 total square feet of living area

Open and spacious living and dining areas for family gatherings

Well-organized kitchen has an abundance of cabinetry and a built-in pantry

Roomy master bath features a double-bowl vanity

3 bedrooms, 2 baths, 2-car drive under garage

Basement foundation

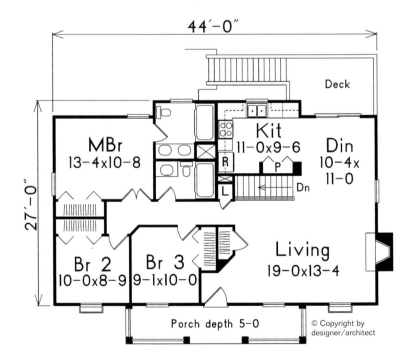

© Copyright by designer/architect

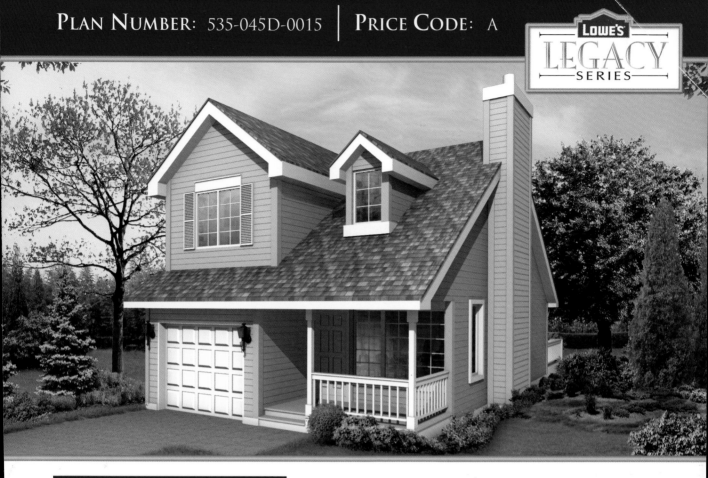

SPECIAL FEATURES

977 total square feet of living area

Comfortable living room features a vaulted ceiling, fireplace, plant shelf and coat closet

Both bedrooms are located on the second floor and share a bath with double-bowl vanity and linen closet

Sliding glass doors in the dining room provide access to the deck

2 bedrooms, 1 1/2 baths, 1-car garage

Basement foundation

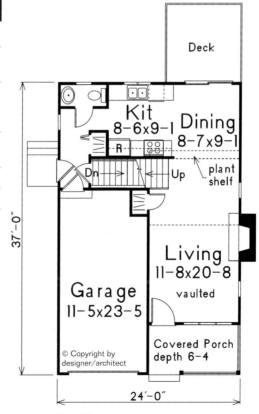

Deck

Kit
8-6x9-1

Dining
8-7x9-1

R

Dn   Up

plant shelf

Living
11-8x20-8
vaulted

Garage
11-5x23-5

© Copyright by designer/architect

Covered Porch
depth 6-4

37'-0"

24'-0"

First Floor
545 sq. ft.

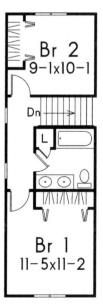

Br 2
9-1x10-1

Dn

L

Br 1
11-5x11-2

Second Floor
432 sq. ft.

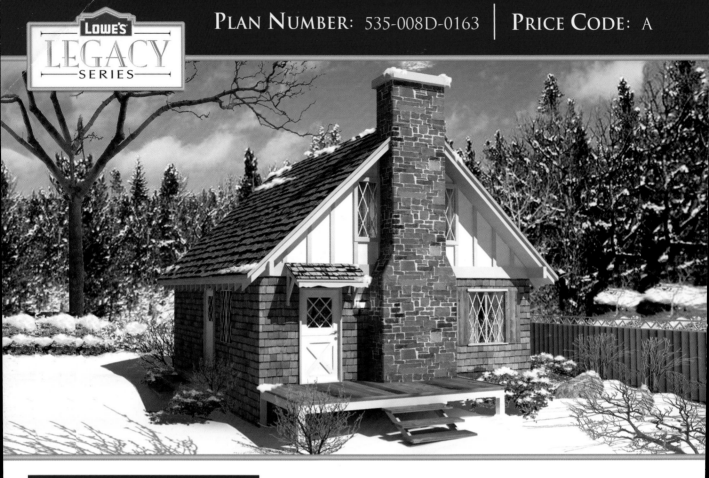

SPECIAL FEATURES

1,280 total square feet of living area

A front porch deck, ornate porch roof, massive stone fireplace and Old-English windows all generate an inviting appearance

The large living room accesses the kitchen and spacious dining area

Two spacious bedrooms with ample closet space comprise the second floor

4 bedrooms, 2 baths

Basement foundation, drawings also include slab and crawl space foundations

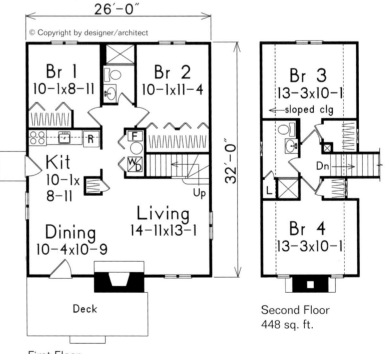

26'-0"

© Copyright by designer/architect

Br 1
10-1x8-11

Br 2
10-1x11-4

Kit
10-1x
8-11

Living
14-11x13-1

Dining
10-4x10-9

Up

32'-0"

Deck

First Floor
832 sq. ft.

Br 3
13-3x10-1
←sloped clg

Dn

L

Br 4
13-3x10-1

Second Floor
448 sq. ft.

SPECIAL FEATURES

- 1,285 total square feet of living area
- Accommodating home with ranch-style porch
- Large storage area on back of home
- Master bedroom includes dressing area, private bath and built-in bookcase
- Kitchen features pantry, breakfast bar and complete view to the dining room
- 2" x 6" exterior walls available, please order plan #535-001D-0119
- 3 bedrooms, 2 baths
- Crawl space foundation, drawings also include basement and slab foundations

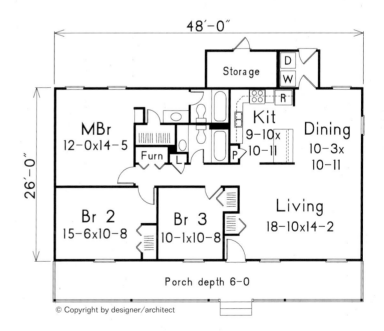

48´-0˝

26´-0˝

Storage

MBr
12-0x14-5

Furn

Kit
9-10x
10-11

Dining
10-3x
10-11

Br 2
15-6x10-8

Br 3
10-1x10-8

Living
18-10x14-2

Porch depth 6-0

© Copyright by designer/architect

SPECIAL FEATURES

2,141 total square feet of living area

A fireplace warms the adjoining great room, kitchen and breakfast area

A covered porch provides outdoor entertaining space

The master bedroom enjoys a coffered ceiling, two closets, a bath and a private study

Each secondary bedroom features a walk-in closet

3 bedrooms, 2 1/2 baths, 3-car garage

Basement foundation

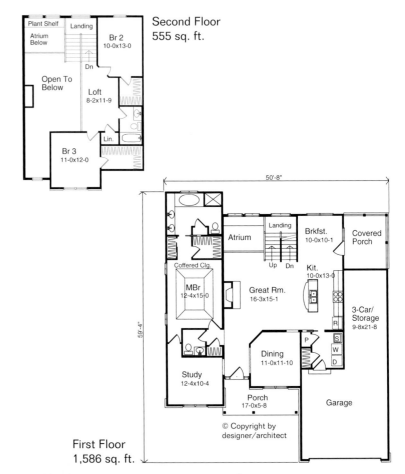

Second Floor
555 sq. ft.

First Floor
1,586 sq. ft.

© Copyright by designer/architect

SPECIAL FEATURES

1,220 total square feet of living area

A vaulted ceiling adds luxury to the living room and master bedroom

Spacious living room is accented with a large fireplace and hearth

Gracious dining area is adjacent to the convenient wrap-around kitchen

Washer and dryer are handy to the bedrooms

Covered porch entry adds appeal

Rear deck adjoins dining area

3 bedrooms, 2 baths, 2-car drive under garage

Basement foundation

© Copyright by designer/architect

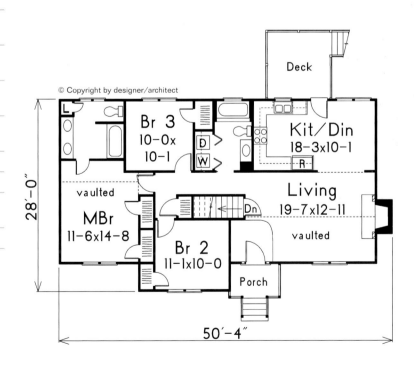

Deck

Br 3
10-0x
10-1

Kit/Din
18-3x10-1

vaulted

MBr
11-6x14-8

Living
19-7x12-11

Br 2
11-1x10-0

vaulted

Porch

28'-0"

50'-4"

SPECIAL FEATURES

1,695 total square feet of living area

Large family room with fireplace makes a spacious, yet cozy gathering place

Garage has convenient workshop space in back

Screened back porch offers protection from sun and insects and connects to the open deck

3 bedrooms, 3 baths, 2-car garage

Basement foundation

Second Floor
816 sq. ft.

MASTER SUITE
13'-8" x 15'-0"
Tray Ceiling

BONUS ROOM
19'-8" x 13'-10"
290 Sq. Ft.

BEDROOM 2
12'-2" x 11'-0"

BEDROOM 3
12'-0" x 11'-0"

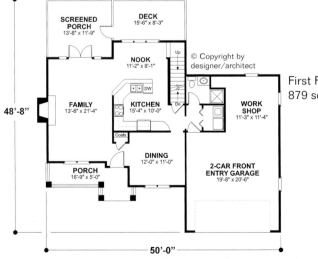

First Floor
879 sq. ft.

SCREENED PORCH
13'-8" x 11'-9"

DECK
15'-6" x 8'-3"

NOOK
11'-2" x 8'-1"

© Copyright by designer/architect

FAMILY
13'-8" x 21'-4"

KITCHEN
15'-4" x 10'-0"

WORK SHOP
11'-3" x 11'-4"

DINING
12'-0" x 11'-0"

PORCH
16'-9" x 5'-0"

2-CAR FRONT ENTRY GARAGE
19'-8" x 20'-6"

48'-8"

50'-0"

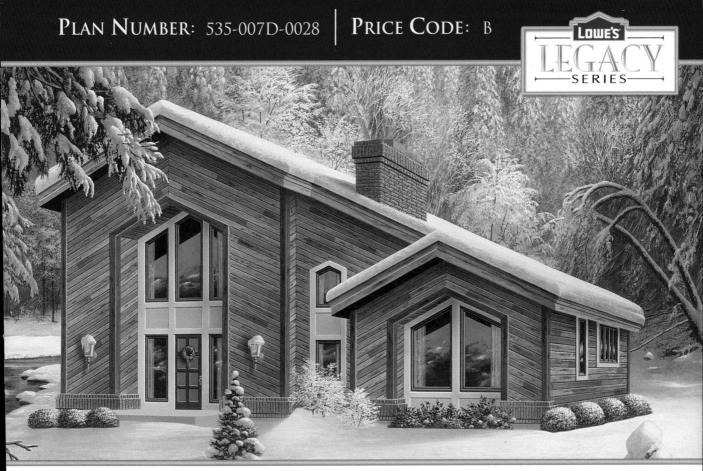

SPECIAL FEATURES

1,711 total square feet of living area

Entry leads to a vaulted great room with exposed beams, two-story window wall, fireplace, wet bar and balcony

Bayed breakfast room shares the fireplace and joins a sun-drenched kitchen and deck

Vaulted first floor master bedroom features a double-door entry, two closets and bookshelves

Spiral stairs and a balcony dramatize the loft that doubles as a spacious second bedroom

2 bedrooms, 2 1/2 baths

Basement foundation

Second Floor
397 sq. ft.

Rear View

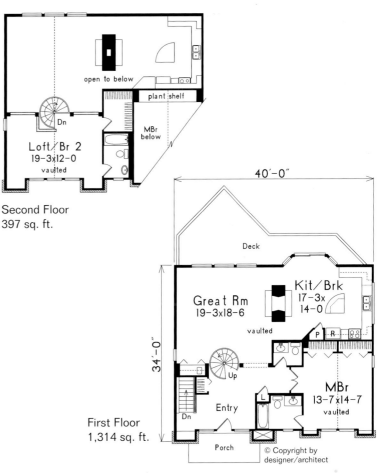

First Floor
1,314 sq. ft.

© Copyright by designer/architect

SPECIAL FEATURES

1,769 total square feet of living area

Living room boasts an elegant cathedral ceiling and fireplace

U-shaped kitchen and dining area combine for easy living

Secondary bedrooms include double closets

Secluded master bedroom features a sloped ceiling, large walk-in closet and private bath

2" x 6" exterior walls available, please order plan #535-001D-0124

3 bedrooms, 2 baths

Basement foundation, drawings also include crawl space and slab foundations

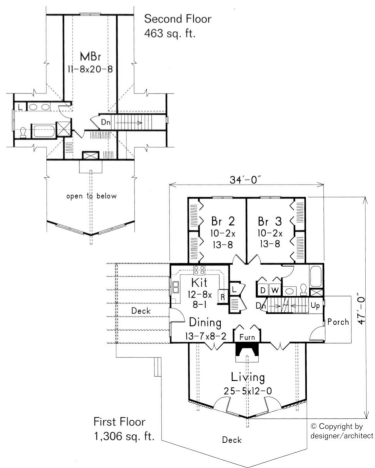

SPECIAL FEATURES

1,973 total square feet of living area

This country colonial offers a grand-sized living room with views to the front and rear of the home

Living room features a cozy fireplace and accesses the master bedroom complete with a walk-in closet and compartmented bath

Laundry room with half bath and coat closet is convenient to the garage

Second floor is comprised of two large bedrooms and a full bath

3 bedrooms, 2 1/2 baths, 2-car garage

Partial basement/crawl space foundation

Second Floor
636 sq. ft.

First Floor
1,337 sq. ft.

© Copyright by designer/architect

LEGACY
SERIES

SPECIAL FEATURES

1,000 total square feet of living area

Large mud room has a separate
covered porch entrance

Full-length covered front porch

Bedrooms are on opposite sides
of the home for privacy

Vaulted ceiling creates an open
and spacious feeling

2" x 6" exterior walls available,
please order plan #535-058D-0085

2 bedrooms, 1 bath

Crawl space foundation

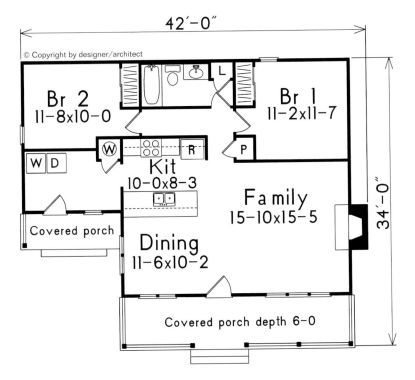

42'-0"

© Copyright by designer/architect

Br 2
11-8x10-0

Br 1
11-2x11-7

W D

Kit
10-0x8-3

Family
15-10x15-5

34'-0"

Covered porch

Dining
11-6x10-2

Covered porch depth 6-0

SPECIAL FEATURES

1,740 total square feet of living area

The dining room boasts a coffered ceiling and specially treated ceilings grace the living room and master bedroom

Master bedroom features a large bath with walk-in closet, double-vanity, separate shower and tub

Both secondary bedrooms have ample closet space

Large breakfast area is convenient to the laundry closet, pantry and rear deck

3 bedrooms, 2 baths, 2-car drive under garage

Basement foundation

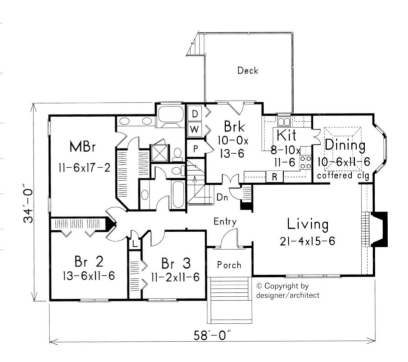

© Copyright by designer/architect

SPECIAL FEATURES

1,941 total square feet of living area

Interesting roof lines and a spacious front porch with flanking stonework help to fashion this beautiful country home

The vaulted great room has a separate entry and bayed dining area suitable for a large family and friends

The master bedroom enjoys a big walk-in closet and a gracious bath

Four additional bedrooms complete the home, one of which is ideal for a study off the great room

5 bedrooms, 3 baths, 2-car side entry drive under garage

Walk-out basement foundation

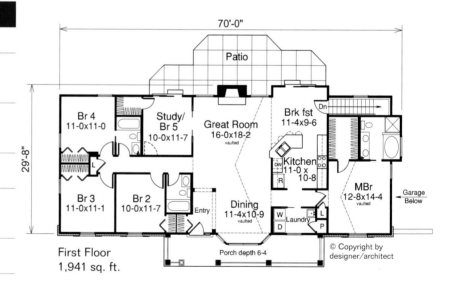

First Floor
1,941 sq. ft.

© Copyright by designer/architect

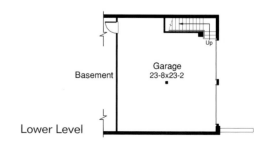

Lower Level

SPECIAL FEATURES

1,230 total square feet of living area

Spacious living room accesses the huge deck

Bedroom #3 features a balcony overlooking the deck

Kitchen with dining area accesses the outdoors

Washer and dryer are tucked under the stairs for space efficiency

3 bedrooms, 1 bath

Crawl space foundation, drawings also include slab foundation

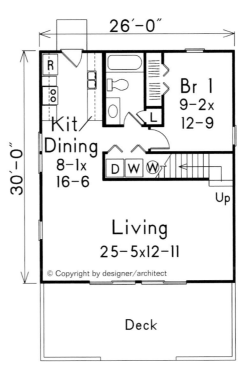

26'-0"

30'-0"

R

Kit
Dining
8-1x
16-6

D W W

Br 1
9-2x
12-9

L

Living
25-5x12-11

Up

© Copyright by designer/architect

Deck

First Floor
780 sq. ft.

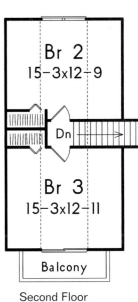

Br 2
15-3x12-9

Dn

Br 3
15-3x12-11

Balcony

Second Floor
450 sq. ft.

Special Features

1,013 total square feet of living area

Vaulted ceilings can be found in both the family room and kitchen with the dining area just beyond the breakfast bar

Plant shelf above kitchen is a special feature

Oversized utility room has space for a full-size washer and dryer

Hall bath is centrally located with easy access from both bedrooms

2" x 6" exterior walls available, please order plan #535-058D-0073

2 bedrooms, 1 bath

Slab foundation

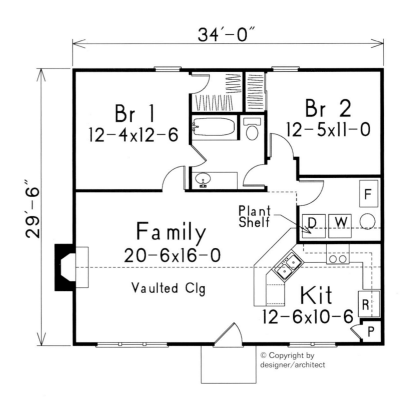

© Copyright by designer/architect

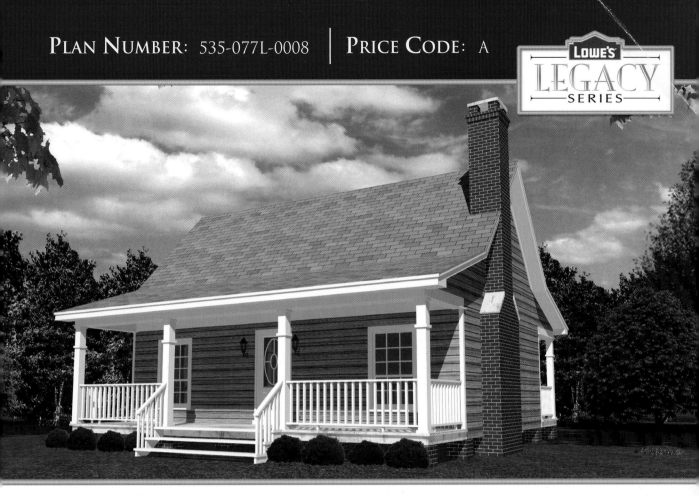

SPECIAL FEATURES

- 600 total square feet of living area

- This small home features a spacious living room that connects to the efficient kitchen with a raised snack bar

- The kitchen and bedroom access the rear porch and covered or screened porch that offer exceptional outdoor living space

- A bonus room is provided for a hobby room or second bedroom

- 1 bedroom, 1 bath

- Slab foundation, drawings also include basement and crawl space foundations

Rear View

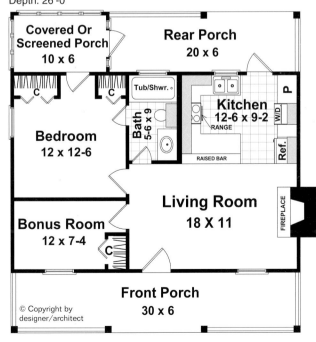

Width: 31'-8"
Depth: 26'-0"

Covered Or Screened Porch
10 x 6

Rear Porch
20 x 6

Bedroom
12 x 12-6

Bath
5-6 x 9

Tub/Shwr.

Kitchen
12-6 x 9-2

RANGE

W/D

Ref.

P

RAISED BAR

Living Room
18 X 11

FIREPLACE

Bonus Room
12 x 7-4

C

Front Porch
30 x 6

© Copyright by designer/architect

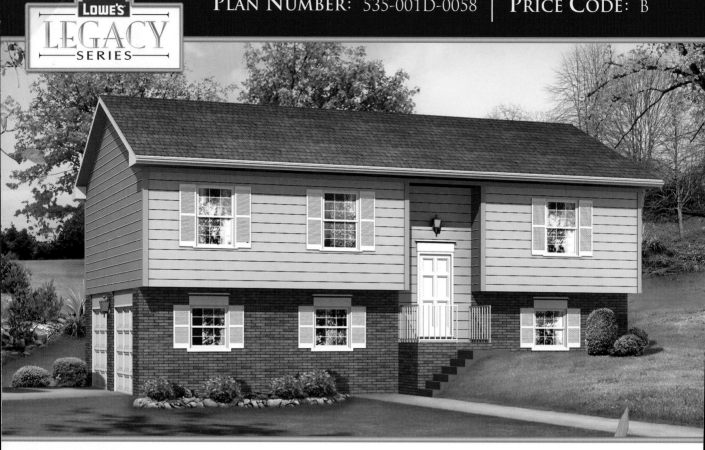

LOWE'S
LEGACY
SERIES

SPECIAL FEATURES

1,720 total square feet of living area

Lower level includes large family room with laundry area and half bath

L-shaped kitchen has a convenient serving bar and pass-through to dining area

Private half bath in master bedroom

3 bedrooms, 1 full bath, 2 half baths, 2-car drive under garage

Basement foundation

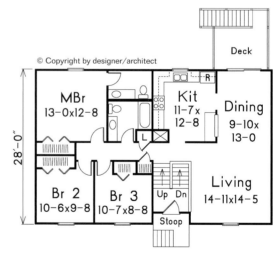

© Copyright by designer/architect

Deck

First Floor
1,218 sq. ft.

MBr
13-0x12-8

Kit
11-7x
12-8

Dining
9-10x
13-0

28'-0"

Br 2
10-6x9-8

Br 3
10-7x8-8

Up Dn

Living
14-11x14-5

Stoop

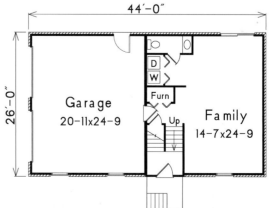

44'-0"

Lower Level
502 sq. ft.

26'-0"

Garage
20-11x24-9

D
W

Furn

Up

Family
14-7x24-9

LOWE'S
LEGACY
SERIES

SPECIAL FEATURES

1,739 total square feet of living area

Energy efficient home with
2" x 6" exterior walls

The living room features a cathedral
ceiling and fireplace that also
warms adjoining rooms

Kitchen with center island provides
an abundance of counterspace and
connects with the dining area

The laundry area serves as the entrance
to the home from the garage

3 bedrooms, 2 1/2 baths, 2-car garage

Basement foundation

SPECIAL FEATURES

1,578 total square feet of living area

Plenty of closet, linen and storage space

Covered porches in the front and rear of home add charm to this design

Open floor plan has a unique angled layout

3 bedrooms, 2 baths, 2-car garage

Basement foundation

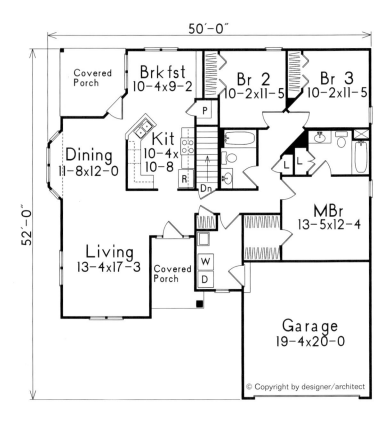

SPECIAL FEATURES

1,752 total square feet of living area

9' ceilings in the eating area and great room make the house feel more open, and the tray ceiling effect in the great room adds a touch of elegance

French doors lead from the eating area onto the charming covered porch

The luxurious master bedroom features a vaulted ceiling and a great view of the backyard

3 bedrooms, 2 baths, 2-car side entry garage

Slab foundation, drawings also include basement and crawl space foundations

© Copyright by designer/architect

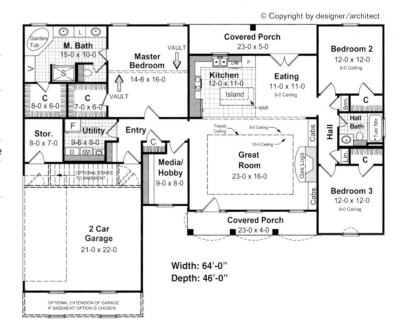

Width: 64'-0"
Depth: 46'-0"

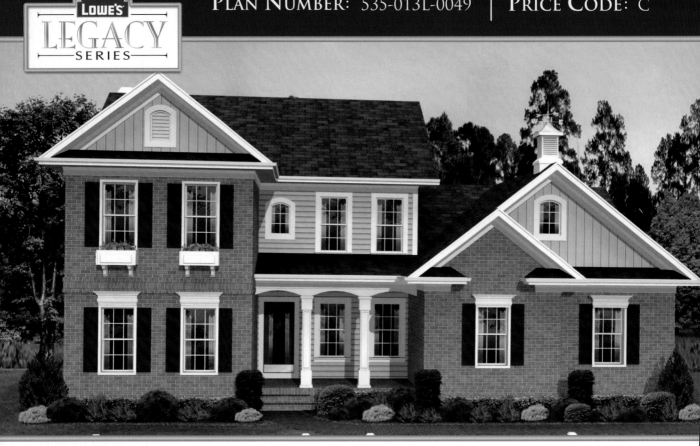

SPECIAL FEATURES

1,944 total square feet of living area

Kitchen opens to nook and dining room for easy meal access

Combined pantry and laundry room connect the home to the garage and workshop

Large master suite has a spacious closet with plenty of room to hang clothes as well as store linens

Sunny guest bedroom with large closet and full bath creates a welcoming room for visitors

4 bedrooms, 3 baths, 3-car side entry garage

Basement foundation

Second Floor
925 sq. ft.

First Floor
1,019 sq. ft.

Lowe's
LEGACY
SERIES

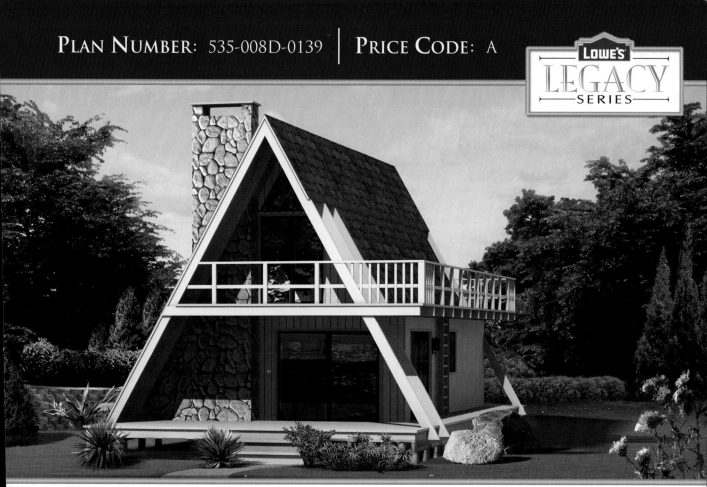

SPECIAL FEATURES

1,272 total square feet of living area

Stone fireplace accents living room

Spacious kitchen includes snack
bar overlooking the living room

First floor bedroom is roomy and secluded

Plenty of closet space for second floor
bedrooms plus a generous balcony
which wraps around the second floor

3 bedrooms, 1 1/2 baths

Crawl space foundation

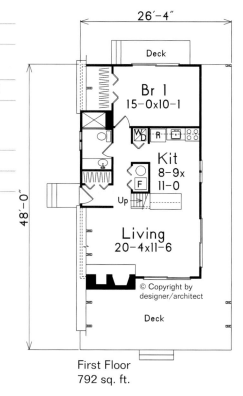

26'-4"

Deck

48'-0"

Br 1
15-0x10-1

Kit
8-9x
11-0

Up

Living
20-4x11-6

© Copyright by
designer/architect

Deck

First Floor
792 sq. ft.

Br 2
14-6x9-7

Dn

Br 3
14-6x11-5
sloped clg

Balcony

Second Floor
480 sq. ft.

Lowe's
LEGACY
SERIES

SPECIAL FEATURES

1,400 total square feet of living area

Master bedroom is secluded for privacy

The large utility room has additional cabinet space

Covered porch provides an outdoor seating area

Roof dormers add great curb appeal

Living room and master bedroom feature vaulted ceilings

Oversized two-car garage has storage space

3 bedrooms, 2 baths, 2-car garage

Basement foundation, drawings also include crawl space foundation

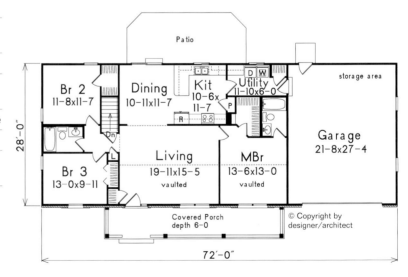

Patio

Br 2
11-8x11-7

Dining
10-11x11-7

Kit
10-6x
11-7

Utility
11-10x6-0

storage area

28'-0"

Dn

Living
19-11x15-5
vaulted

MBr
13-6x13-0
vaulted

Garage
21-8x27-4

Br 3
13-0x9-11

Covered Porch
depth 6-0

© Copyright by designer/architect

72'-0"

SPECIAL FEATURES

- 1,277 total square feet of living area

- Vaulted ceilings grace the master bedroom, great room, kitchen and dining room

- Laundry closet is located near the bedrooms for convenience

- Compact, yet efficient kitchen

- 2" x 6" exterior walls available, please order plan #535-058D-0090

- 3 bedrooms, 2 baths, 2-car garage

- Basement foundation

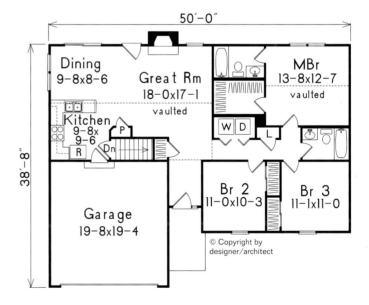

50'-0"

38'-8"

Dining
9-8x8-6

Great Rm
18-0x17-1
vaulted

MBr
13-8x12-7
vaulted

Kitchen
9-8x
9-6

W D

L

Br 2
11-0x10-3

Br 3
11-1x11-0

Garage
19-8x19-4

© Copyright by
designer/architect

SPECIAL FEATURES

1,456 total square feet of living area

A beautiful fireplace is the focal point in the cozy family room

The formal dining room, located between the kitchen and family room, is positioned perfectly for entertaining

The bonus room above the garage has an additional 182 square feet of living area

3 bedrooms, 2 1/2 baths, 2-car garage

Basement foundation

MASTER BEDRM 15x13

BONUS ROOM 14x13

BEDRM 3 10x12

BEDRM 2 10x13

Second Floor 768 sq. ft.

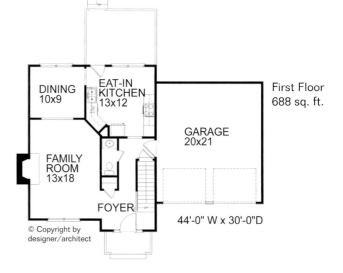

DINING 10x9

EAT-IN KITCHEN 13x12

GARAGE 20x21

FAMILY ROOM 13x18

FOYER

First Floor 688 sq. ft.

44'-0" W x 30'-0"D

© Copyright by designer/architect

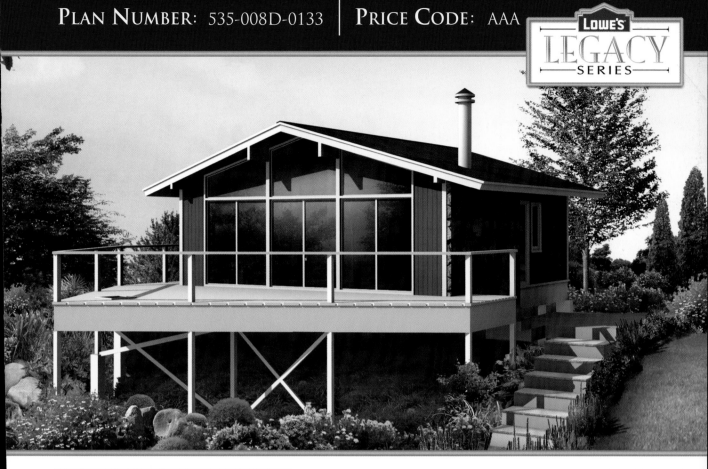

SPECIAL FEATURES

624 total square feet of living area

The combination of stone, vertical siding, lots of glass and a low roof line creates a cozy retreat

Vaulted living area features a free-standing fireplace that heats the adjacent stone wall

Efficient kitchen includes a dining area and view onto an angular deck

Two bedrooms share a hall bath with shower

2 bedrooms, 1 bath

Pier foundation

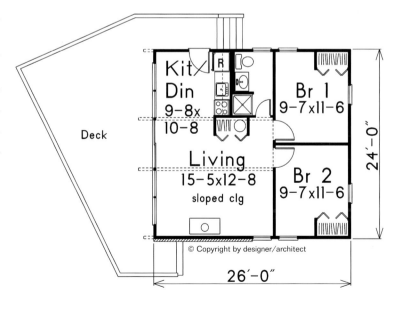

© Copyright by designer/architect

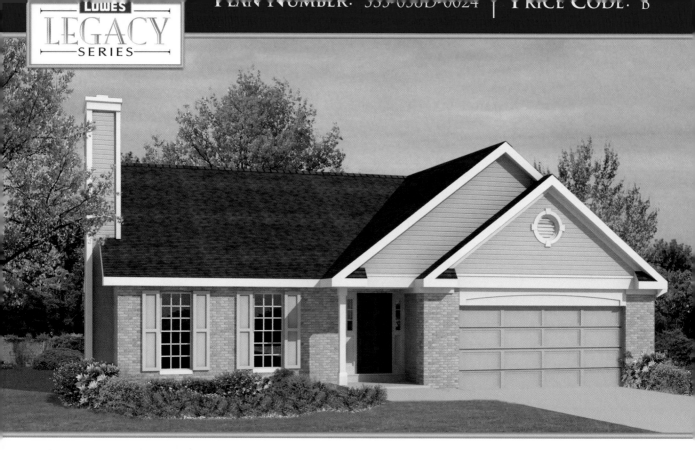

SPECIAL FEATURES

1,598 total square feet of living area

Additional storage area in garage

Double-door entry into master bedroom with luxurious master bath

Entry opens into large family room with vaulted ceiling and open stairway to basement

3 bedrooms, 2 baths, 2-car garage

Basement foundation

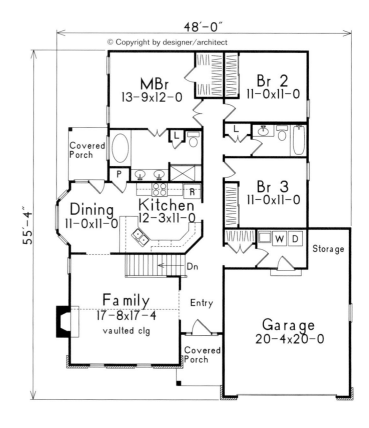

48'-0"

© Copyright by designer/architect

55'-4"

MBr
13-9x12-0

Br 2
11-0x11-0

Covered
Porch

L

L

P

Dining
11-0x11-0

Kitchen
12-3x11-0

R

Br 3
11-0x11-0

W D

Storage

Dn

Family
17-8x17-4
vaulted clg

Entry

Garage
20-4x20-0

Covered
Porch

SPECIAL FEATURES

2,000 total square feet of living area

A popular outdoor kitchen is incorporated into the covered rear porch perfect for year-round outdoor enjoyment with family and friends

Enter double doors off the great room to find a media/hobby room with plenty of storage space

Double walk-in closets in the master bedroom and bath help keep the homeowners organized

The bonus room above the garage has an additional 334 square feet of living area

3 bedrooms, 2 1/2 baths, 2-car side entry garage

Slab foundation, drawings also include crawl space foundation

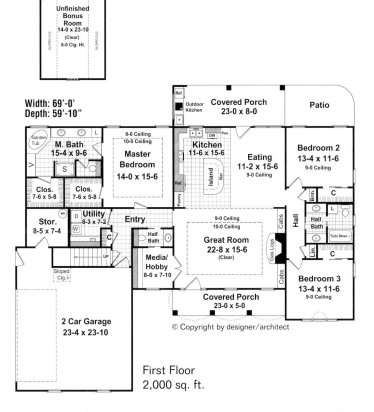

Optional
Second Floor

Unfinished Bonus Room
14-0 x 23-10
(Clear)
8-0 Clg. Ht.

Width: 69'-0"
Depth: 59'-10"

Covered Porch
23-0 x 8-0

Patio

Outdoor Kitchen

M. Bath
15-4 x 9-6

Master Bedroom
14-0 x 15-6

9-0 Ceiling
10-0 Ceiling

Kitchen
11-6 x 15-6

Eating
11-2 x 15-6
9-0 Ceiling

Bedroom 2
13-4 x 11-6
9-0 Ceiling

Clos.
7-6 x 5-8

Clos.
7-6 x 5-8

Island

Hall

Hall Bath

Stor.
8-5 x 7-4

Utility
8-3 x 7-2

Entry

9-0 Ceiling
10-0 Ceiling

Great Room
22-8 x 15-6
(Clear)

Gas Logs

Half Bath

Media/Hobby
8-0 x 7-10

Bedroom 3
13-4 x 11-6
9-0 Ceiling

Sloped Clg.

2 Car Garage
23-4 x 23-10

Covered Porch
23-0 x 5-0

© Copyright by designer/architect

First Floor
2,000 sq. ft.

SPECIAL FEATURES

1,270 total square feet of living area

Spacious living area features angled stairs, vaulted ceiling, exciting fireplace and deck access

Master bedroom includes a walk-in closet and private bath

Dining and living rooms join to create an open atmosphere

Eat-in kitchen has a convenient pass-through to the dining room

3 bedrooms, 2 baths, 2-car garage

Basement foundation

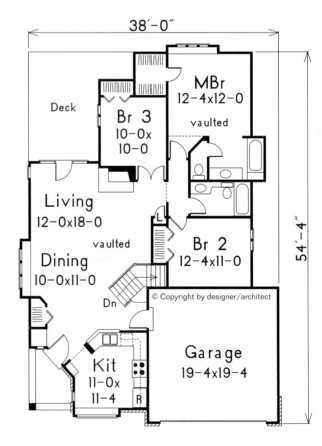

38'-0"

Deck

MBr
12-4x12-0
vaulted

Br 3
10-0x
10-0

Living
12-0x18-0
vaulted

Br 2
12-4x11-0

Dining
10-0x11-0

© Copyright by designer/architect

Dn

54'-4"

Kit
11-0x
11-4

Garage
19-4x19-4

LOWE'S LEGACY SERIES

SPECIAL FEATURES

2,197 total square feet of living area

The master suite features a tray ceiling and a bath with his & her vanities and a walk-in closet

A triple window unit brightens the breakfast room and kitchen

A 14' ceiling, corner fireplace, and lots of glass create a magnificent family room

The secondary bedrooms measure nearly 14' x 11' and share a Jack and Jill bath

3 bedrooms, 2 1/2 baths, 2-car side entry drive under garage

Basement foundation

© Copyright by designer/architect

BEDROOM 3
13'8" x 11'0"

DECK
16'4" x 10'4"

BREAKFAST
12'8" x 10'0"

TRAY CEILING

MASTER BDRM
15'8" x 16'0"

14' HIGH CEILING

KITCHEN
12'8" x 10'8"

FAMILY ROOM
17'0" x 18'4"

BEDROOM 2
13'8" x 11'0"

DINING
12'8" x 11'0"

LIVING
10'8" x 11'8"

11' HIGH CEILING

42'-0"

64'-4"

LEGACY
SERIES

SPECIAL FEATURES

1,137 total square feet of living area

Cleverly designed two-story is disguised as an attractive one-story home

The spacious and dramatic entry features a vaulted ceiling, coat closet with plant shelf above and an ascending stair to the second floor

The living room with fireplace is open to the bayed dining area and functional L-shaped kitchen furnished with an island counter and adjacent laundry room

The optional finished lower level includes a family room, hall bath and third bedroom with walk-in closet and allows for an extra 591 square feet of living area

2 bedrooms, 1 1/2 baths, 2-car garage

Walk-out basement foundation

30'-0"

Deck

Dine

Kitchen
9-0x11-4

Living Room
20-4x13-1

41'-0"

DN

UP

Entry

Garage
21-4x21-4

Porch

© Copyright by designer/architect

First Floor
621 sq. ft.

Master Bedroom
14-8x13-1

Bedroom #2
12-1x9-0

Hall

DN

Attic Storage

Vaulted Entry below

Plant shelf below

Second Floor
516 sq. ft.

Patio

Family Room
14-0x13-0

Bedroom #3
13-9x10-9

UP

F WH

Optional
Lower Level

LOWE'S
LEGACY
SERIES

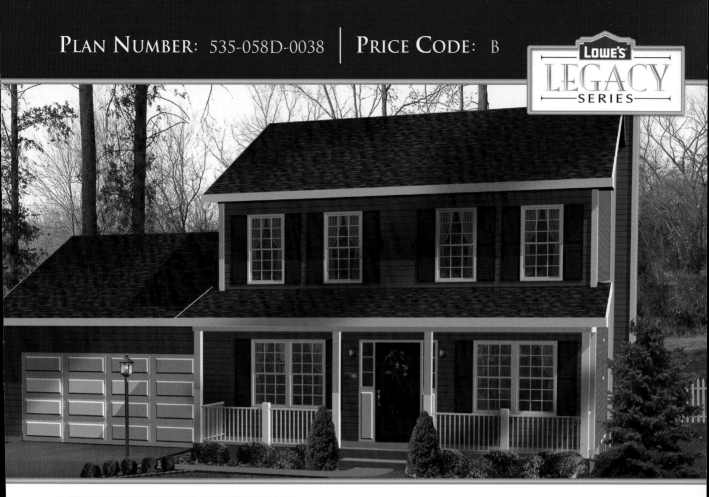

SPECIAL FEATURES

1,680 total square feet of living area

Compact and efficient layout
in an affordable package

Second floor has three bedrooms
all with oversized closets

All bedrooms are located on the
second floor for privacy

3 bedrooms, 2 1/2 baths, 2-car garage

Basement foundation

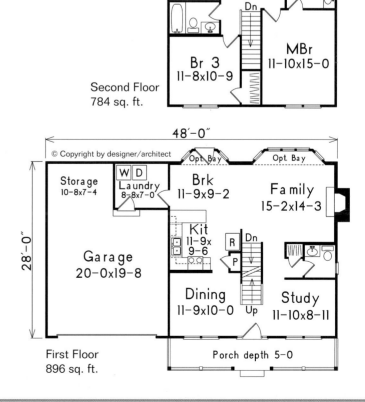

Br 2
11-8x10-9

L

Dn

MBr
11-10x15-0

Br 3
11-8x10-9

Second Floor
784 sq. ft.

48'-0"

© Copyright by designer/architect

Opt. Bay   Opt. Bay

Storage
10-8x7-4

W D
Laundry
8-8x7-0

Brk
11-9x9-2

Family
15-2x14-3

28'-0"

Kit
11-9x
9-6

R   Dn

Garage
20-0x19-8

P

Dining
11-9x10-0   Up

Study
11-10x8-11

First Floor
896 sq. ft.

Porch depth 5-0

SPECIAL FEATURES

1,459 total square feet of living area

Cozy vaulted breakfast room is located between the kitchen and the formal dining room

Two decks extend off the first floor master bedroom and sunroom creating a relaxing retreat

Future space on the lower level has an additional 520 square feet of living area

3 bedrooms, 2 baths, 2-car garage

Slab foundation

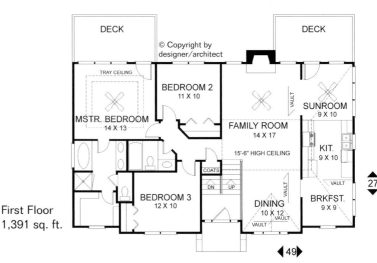

First Floor
1,391 sq. ft.

Lower Level
68 sq. ft.

TO ORDER SEE PAGE 288

| CALL TOLL-FREE 1-877-379-3420

SPECIAL FEATURES

1,851 total square feet of living area

High-impact entrance to great room also leads directly to the second floor

First floor master bedroom suite with corner window and walk-in closet

Kitchen/breakfast room has a center work island and pass-through to the dining room

Second floor bedrooms share a bath

4 bedrooms, 2 1/2 baths, 2-car garage

Basement foundation

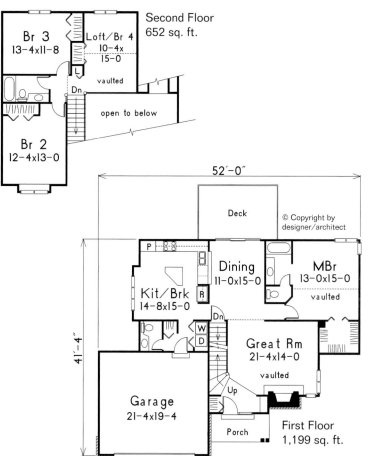

Second Floor
652 sq. ft.

Br 3
13-4x11-8

Loft/Br 4
10-4x
15-0
vaulted

Dn

open to below

Br 2
12-4x13-0

52'-0"

Deck

© Copyright by
designer/architect

P

Dining
11-0x15-0

MBr
13-0x15-0
vaulted

Kit/Brk
14-8x15-0

R

Dn

W
D

Great Rm
21-4x14-0
vaulted

41'-4"

Garage
21-4x19-4

Up

Porch

First Floor
1,199 sq. ft.

SPECIAL FEATURES

2,150 total square feet of living area

The centrally located kitchen with pantry serves the breakfast area and formal dining room with ease

The study located at the front of the house would make an ideal home office

A coffered ceiling, two walk-in closets and a corner whirlpool tub enhance the master bedroom

3 bedrooms, 2 1/2 baths, 3-car garage

Basement foundation

Second Floor
499 sq. ft.

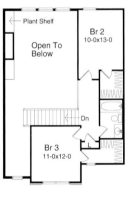

Plant Shelf

Open To Below

Br 2
10-0x13-0

Dn

Br 3
11-0x12-0

50'-8"

60'-0"

Great Room
14-3x21-3

Breakfast
10-3x8-11

Screened Porch
10-0x12-0

Coffered Ceiling

MBr
12-4x15-0

Kit.
10-3x12-6

3-Car
9-8x21-8

Up

Dn

Foyer

Dining
11-0x11-10

W
D

Study
12-4x13-5

Covered Porch

Garage
19-4x19-8

© Copyright by designer/architect

First Floor
1,651 sq. ft.

SPECIAL FEATURES

1,160 total square feet of living area

U-shaped kitchen includes a breakfast bar and convenient laundry area

Master bedroom features private half bath and large closet

Dining room has outdoor access

Dining and great rooms combine to create an open living atmosphere

3 bedrooms, 1 1/2 baths

Crawl space foundation, drawings also include basement and slab foundations

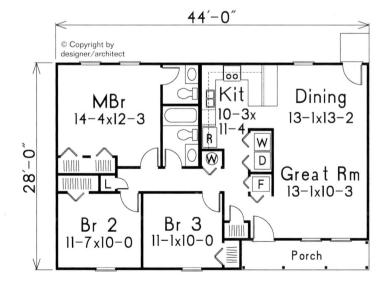

44'-0"

28'-0"

© Copyright by designer/architect

MBr
14-4x12-3

Kit
10-3x
11-4

Dining
13-1x13-2

Great Rm
13-1x10-3

Br 2
11-7x10-0

Br 3
11-1x10-0

Porch

Lowe's LEGACY SERIES

SPECIAL FEATURES

1,458 total square feet of living area

A convenient snack bar joins the kitchen with breakfast room

Large living room has a fireplace, plenty of windows, vaulted ceiling and nearby plant shelf

Master bedroom offers a private bath, walk-in closet, plant shelf and coffered ceiling

Corner windows provide abundant light in the breakfast room

3 bedrooms, 2 baths, 2-car garage

Crawl space foundation, drawings also include slab foundation

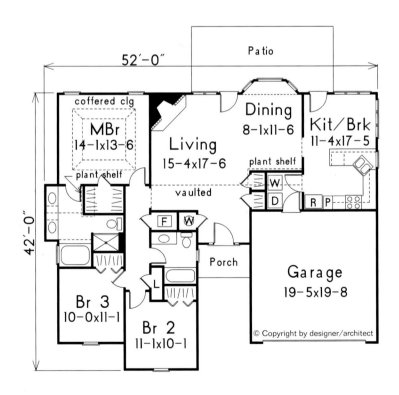

© Copyright by designer/architect

LOWE'S
LEGACY
SERIES

SPECIAL FEATURES

1,798 total square feet of living area

A gourmet kitchen, casual dining room and a rear covered porch overlooking the pool make this home a delight for entertaining

The generous master suite features a sitting area and large walk-in closet with separate his and hers sections

The front home office can easily become a guest suite with its own walk-in closet and private bath access

3 bedrooms, 2 1/2 baths, 2-car side entry garage

Slab foundation

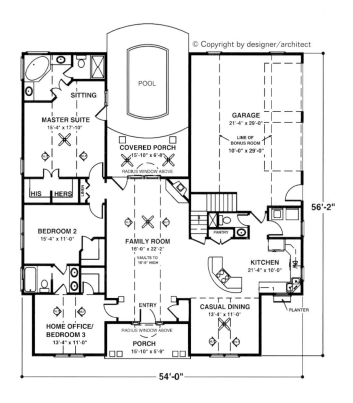

© Copyright by designer/architect

POOL

SITTING

MASTER SUITE
15'-4" x 17'-10"

GARAGE
21'-4" x 29'-0"

LINE OF
BONUS ROOM
10'-0" x 29'-0"

COVERED PORCH
15'-10" x 6'-8"

RADIUS WINDOW ABOVE

HIS   HERS   LINEN

BEDROOM 2
15'-4" x 11'-0"

PANTRY

FAMILY ROOM
16'-0" x 22'-2"
VAULTS TO
18'-6" HIGH

56'-2"

KITCHEN
21'-4" x 10'-0"

PLANTER

ENTRY

CASUAL DINING
13'-4" x 11'-0"

HOME OFFICE/
BEDROOM 3
13'-4" x 11'-0"

RADIUS WINDOW ABOVE

PORCH
15'-10" x 5'-9"

54'-0"

LEGACY SERIES
LOWE'S

SPECIAL FEATURES

1,026 total square feet of living area

A one-story look, clerestory roof dormer and nice symmetry all help to create this handsome exterior

The cozy front porch invites you into a nice-sized living room with entry area and coat closet

Adjacent to the U-shaped kitchen with built-in pantry is the dining room which enjoys views of the patio area through a large bay window

The laundry room with closet is conveniently located and accesses one of the two garages

1 bedroom, 1 1/2 baths, 4-car garage

Slab foundation

Bedroom
17-3x13-9

Hall

Second Floor
439 sq. ft.

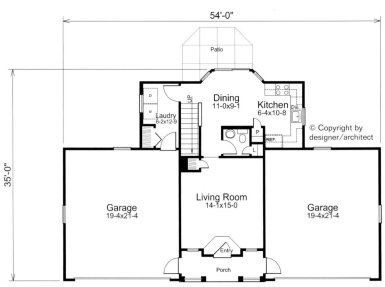

54'-0"

35'-0"

Patio

Laudry
6-2x12-9

Dining
11-0x9-1

Kitchen
6-4x10-8

© Copyright by designer/architect

Garage
19-4x21-4

Living Room
14-1x15-0

Garage
19-4x21-4

Entry

Porch

First Floor
587 sq. ft.

SPECIAL FEATURES

973 total square feet of living area

Side entry garage creates a garage apartment with the look of a two-story home

Sunny breakfast room is positioned between the kitchen and the family room for convenience

Both bedrooms are generously sized

2 bedrooms, 1 bath, 2-car side entry garage with storage

Basement foundation

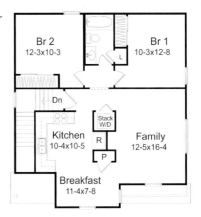

Second Floor
973 sq. ft.

Br 2
12-3x10-3

Br 1
10-3x12-8

L

Dn

Stack
W/D

Kitchen
10-4x10-5

R

Family
12-5x16-4

P

Breakfast
11-4x7-8

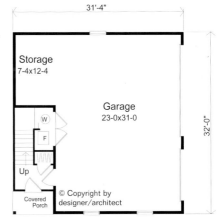

First Floor

31'-4"

Storage
7-4x12-4

Garage
23-0x31-0

32'-0"

W

F

Up

Covered
Porch

© Copyright by
designer/architect

LOWE'S LEGACY SERIES

SPECIAL FEATURES

1,759 total square feet of living area

The striking entry is created by
a unique stair layout, an open
high ceiling and a fireplace

Bonus area over garage, which is included
in the square footage, could easily convert
to a fourth bedroom or activity center

Second floor bedrooms share a
private dressing area and bath

3 bedrooms, 2 1/2 baths, 2-car garage

Basement foundation

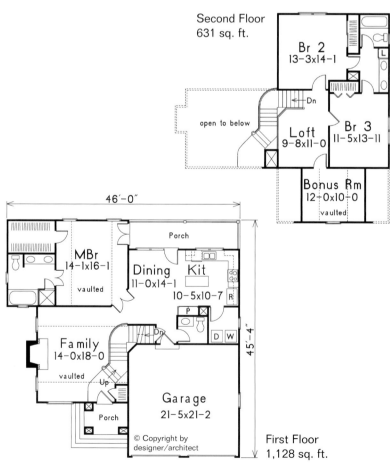

Second Floor
631 sq. ft.

Br 2
13-3x14-1

open to below

Loft
9-8x11-0

Br 3
11-5x13-11

Bonus Rm
12-0x10-0
vaulted

46'-0"

MBr
14-1x16-1
vaulted

Dining
11-0x14-1

Kit
10-5x10-7

Porch

Family
14-0x18-0
vaulted

Garage
21-5x21-2

Porch

45'-4"

© Copyright by
designer/architect

First Floor
1,128 sq. ft.

SPECIAL FEATURES

2,087 total square feet of living area

Family room with breakfast area offers outstanding size

Plan includes a convenient half bath and first floor laundry

Master bedroom enjoys two closets and access to a covered deck

4 bedrooms, 2 1/2 baths, 2-car garage

Basement foundation, drawings also include crawl space and slab foundations

Second Floor
1,042 sq. ft.

Bed 3
13-4x10-0

Bed 2
13-8x13-4

Bed 4/ Sit
11-3x10-0

Master Bed
18-7x12-0

Deck

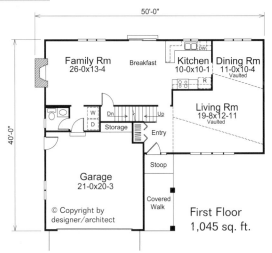

50'-0"

40'-0"

Family Rm
26-0x13-4

Breakfast

Kitchen
10-0x10-1

Dining Rm
11-0x10-4
Vaulted

Living Rm
19-8x12-11
Vaulted

W D

Dn Up

Storage

Entry

Stoop

Garage
21-0x20-3

Covered Walk

© Copyright by designer/architect

First Floor
1,045 sq. ft.

Legacy series

Special Features

2,097 total square feet of living area

Step inside the columned entry to find a formal dining area and quiet home office beyond lovely French doors

With a fireplace, ceiling fan and access to a roomy screened porch through French doors, the family room is the perfect spot to entertain guests

Adjoining this space, the open kitchen creates an atmosphere for both cooking and conversation

4 bedrooms, 3 baths, 2-car garage

Walk-out basement foundation

Second Floor
903 sq. ft.

OPEN BELOW
17'-3" x 18'-3"

SITTING

MASTER SUITE
20'-10" x 14'-9"
TRAY CEILING

CLOSET
10'-7" x 4'-6"

OPTIONAL STORAGE OR MASTER CLOSET
19'-8" x 5'-10"

BEDROOM 2
12'-0" x 11'-0"

BEDROOM 3
12'-0" x 11'-0"

5' HIGH KNEE WALL

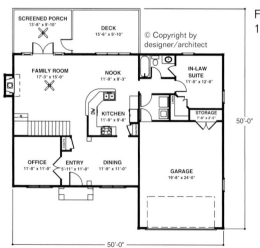

First Floor
1,194 sq. ft.

SCREENED PORCH
13'-8" x 9'-10"

DECK
15'-6" x 9'-10"

© Copyright by designer/architect

FAMILY ROOM
17'-3" x 15'-0"

NOOK
11'-9" x 8'-3"

IN-LAW SUITE
11'-0" x 12'-0"

KITCHEN
11'-9" x 9'-8"

STORAGE
7'-8" x 2'-5"

OFFICE
11'-0" x 11'-0"

ENTRY
5'-11" x 11'-0"

DINING
11'-9" x 11'-0"

GARAGE
19'-8" x 24'-0"

50'-0"

50'-0"

SPECIAL FEATURES

1,440 total square feet of living area

Open floor plan with access to covered porches in front and back

Lots of linen, pantry and closet space throughout

Laundry/mud room between kitchen and garage is a convenient feature

2 bedrooms, 2 baths, 2-car side entry garage

Basement foundation

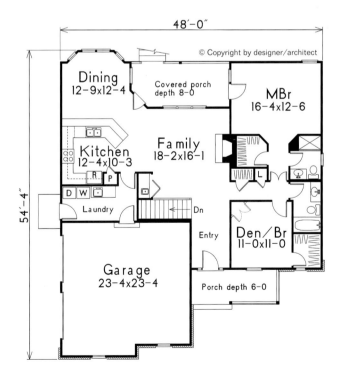

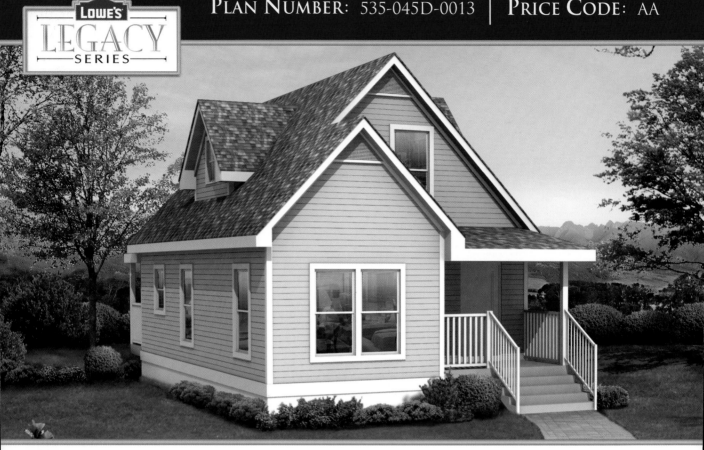

SPECIAL FEATURES

1,085 total square feet of living area

Rear porch provides handy access through the kitchen

Convenient hall linen closet is located on the second floor

Breakfast bar in the kitchen offers additional counterspace

Living and dining rooms combine for open living

3 bedrooms, 2 baths

Basement foundation

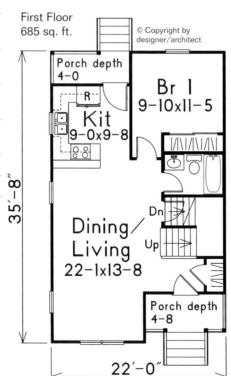

First Floor
685 sq. ft.

© Copyright by designer/architect

Porch depth 4-0

Kit 9-0x9-8

Br 1 9-10x11-5

35'-8"

Dining/ Living 22-1x13-8

Dn

Up

Porch depth 4-8

22'-0"

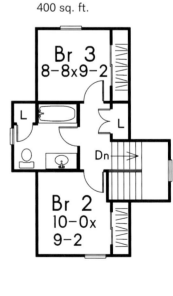

Second Floor
400 sq. ft.

Br 3 8-8x9-2

L

L

Dn

Br 2 10-0x 9-2

SPECIAL FEATURES

1,662 total square feet of living area

The living room becomes an ideal place for family gatherings

Well-organized kitchen includes lots of storage space, a walk-in pantry and plenty of cabinetry

The rear of the home features a versatile back porch for dining or relaxing

Master bedroom has a bay window and private balcony

2 bedrooms, 1 1/2 baths

Basement foundation

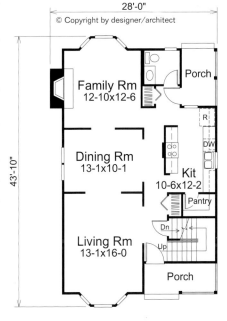

First Floor
1,092 sq. ft.

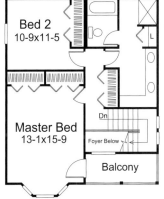

Second Floor
570 sq. ft.

SPECIAL FEATURES

1,803 total square feet of living area

Master bedroom features a raised ceiling and private bath with a walk-in closet, large double-bowl vanity and separate tub and shower

U-shaped kitchen includes a corner sink and convenient pantry

Vaulted living room is complete with a fireplace and built-in cabinet

3 bedrooms, 2 baths, 3-car drive under garage

Basement foundation

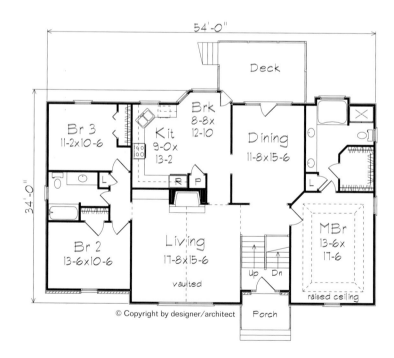

54'-0"

34'-0"

Deck

Br 3
11-2x10-6

Kit
9-0x
13-2

Brk
8-8x
12-10

Dining
11-8x15-6

Br 2
13-6x10-6

Living
17-8x15-6
vaulted

up   Dn

MBr
13-6x
17-6

raised ceiling

Porch

© Copyright by designer/architect

SPECIAL FEATURES

1,207 total square feet of living area

A bay window with access to the outdoors, pantry and island with seating enhance the breakfast area/kitchen

A vaulted ceiling and fireplace add elegance to the family room

Bedrooms are separated from main living areas for privacy

3 bedrooms, 2 baths, 2-car garage

Basement foundation

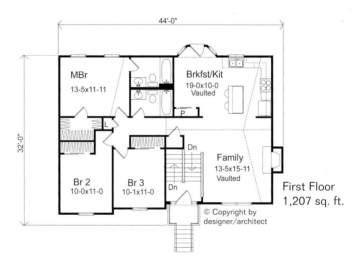

44'-0"

32'-0"

MBr
13-5x11-11

Brkfst/Kit
19-0x10-0
Vaulted

P

Br 2
10-0x11-0

Br 3
10-1x11-0

Dn

Dn

Family
13-5x15-11
Vaulted

First Floor
1,207 sq. ft.

© Copyright by
designer/architect

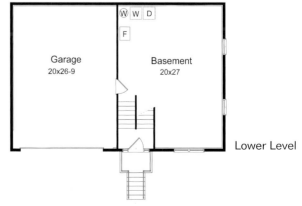

W W D

F

Garage
20x26-9

Basement
20x27

Lower Level

SPECIAL FEATURES

792 total square feet of living area

The living area is entirely open and consists of the kitchen, eating space and family room

An abundance of storage space is offered, including a walk-in pantry and two closets in the bedroom

The covered porch offers an enchanting atmosphere for enjoying the outdoors

1 bedroom, 1 bath, 2-car garage

Slab foundation

Second Floor
792 sq. ft.

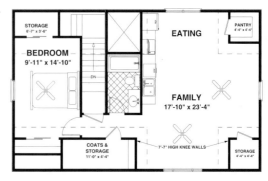

STORAGE
6'-7" x 3'-6"

EATING

PANTRY
4'-4" x 4'-4"

BEDROOM
9'-11" x 14'-10"

DN

FAMILY
17'-10" x 23'-4"

COATS & STORAGE
11'-0" x 4'-4"

7'-7" HIGH KNEE WALLS

STORAGE
4'-4" x 4'-4"

First Floor

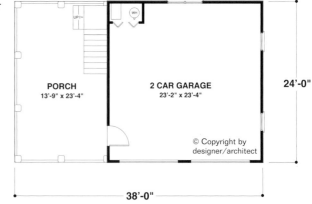

UP

WH

PORCH
13'-9" x 23'-4"

2 CAR GARAGE
23'-2" x 23'-4"

24'-0"

© Copyright by
designer/architect

38'-0"

LOWE'S
LEGACY
SERIES

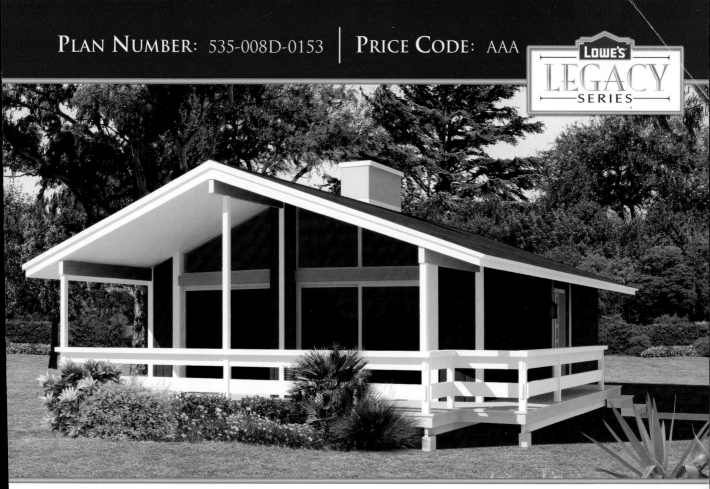

SPECIAL FEATURES

792 total square feet of living area

Attractive exterior features wood posts and beams, wrap-around deck with railing and glass sliding doors with transoms

Kitchen, living and dining areas enjoy sloped ceilings, a cozy fireplace and views over the deck

Two bedrooms share a bath just off the hall

2 bedrooms, 1 bath

Crawl space foundation, drawings also include slab foundation

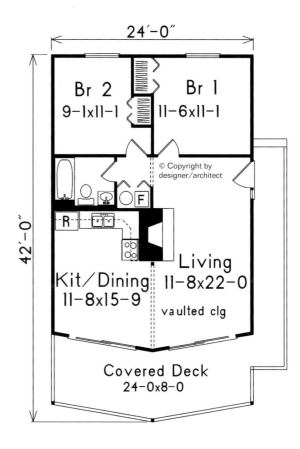

Lowe's LEGACY SERIES

SPECIAL FEATURES

2,080 total square feet of living area

The perfect design to accommodate a sloping site

The generous great room features a vaulted ceiling, large bay window, fireplace and is open to the entry and dining areas

For convenience, the kitchen is a U-shaped style and includes a garden window and built-in pantry

The lower level offers a spacious family room, fourth bedroom, third bath, laundry and oversized garage

4 bedrooms, 3 baths, 2-car drive under garage

Basement foundation

43'-0"

© Copyright by designer/architect

Dn

Deck

33'-0"

Dining
10-0x13-7
vaulted

Kit
9-6 x
11-0

Br 3
9-0x11-0

Br 2
10-11x11-0

Great Rm
15-8x20-9
vaulted

Up Dn
Entry

MBr
14-1x12-7

Porch

First Floor
1,338 sq. ft.

Br 4
11-0x11-7

D
W

Garage
19-2x29-0

Family
16-0x17-6

Up
Entry

Porch

Lower Level
742 sq. ft.

SPECIAL FEATURES

990 total square feet of living area

Wrap-around porch creates a relaxing retreat

Combined family and dining rooms boast a vaulted ceiling

Space for an efficiency washer and dryer unit offers convenience

2" x 6" exterior walls available, please order plan #535-058D-0086

2 bedrooms, 1 bath

Crawl space foundation

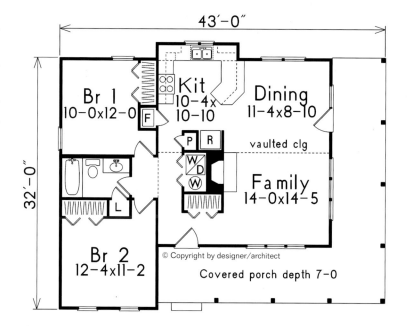

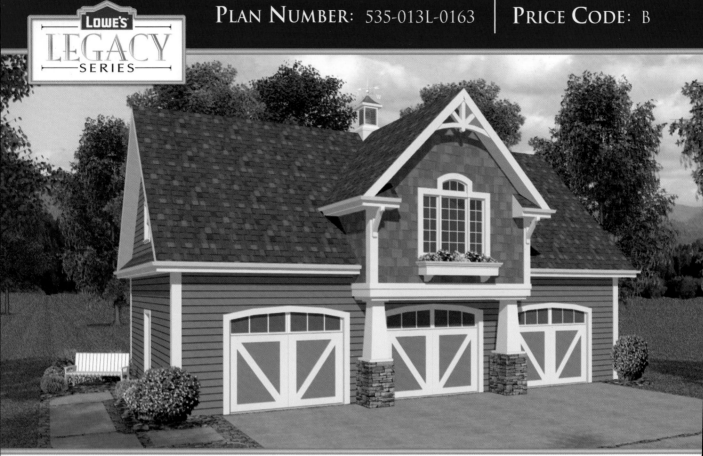

Lowe's LEGACY SERIES

SPECIAL FEATURES

838 total square feet of living area

Stone columns and a planter box decorate the exterior of this lovely apartment home

Inside, the garage conveniently houses a washer/dryer unit

An abundance of storage can be found throughout the unit, including built-in shelves in the family room and a pantry in the kitchen

1 bedroom, 1 bath, 3-car garage

Slab foundation

Second Floor
838 sq. ft.

First Floor

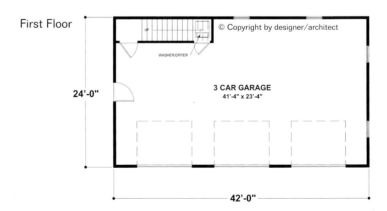

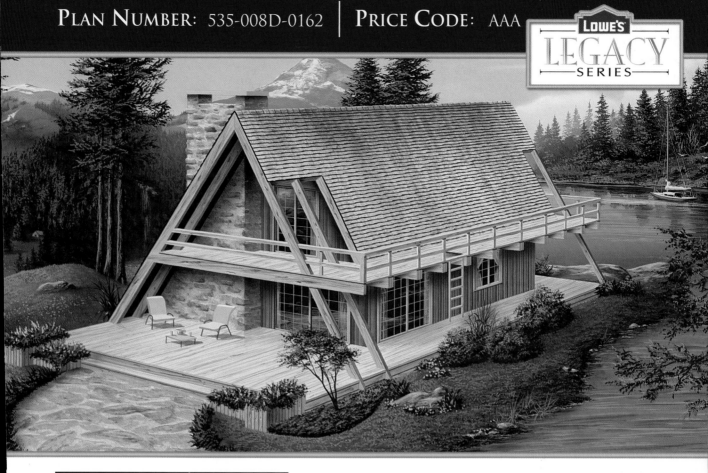

LOWE'S
LEGACY
SERIES

SPECIAL FEATURES

865 total square feet of living area

Central living area provides an enormous amount of space for gathering around the fireplace

The outdoor ladder on the wrap-around deck connects the top deck with the main deck

Kitchen is bright and cheerful with lots of windows and access to the deck

2 bedrooms, 1 bath

Pier foundation

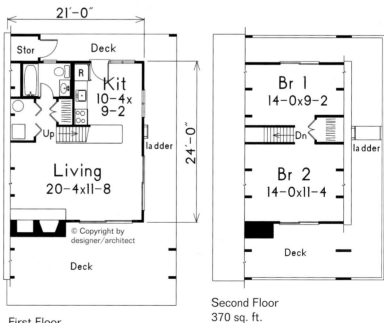

First Floor
495 sq. ft.

Second Floor
370 sq. ft.

SPECIAL FEATURES

1,540 total square feet of living area

Energy efficient home with
2" x 6" exterior walls

Spacious master bedroom has a
large walk-in closet and sweeping
windows overlooking the yard

First floor laundry is conveniently located
between the garage and kitchen

Living room features a cathedral
ceiling and corner fireplace

3 bedrooms, 2 baths, 2-car garage

Basement foundation

© Copyright by designer/architect

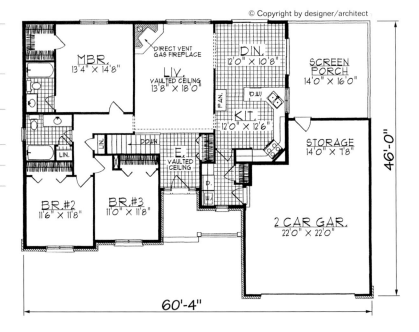

SPECIAL FEATURES

480 total square feet of living area

A wide, covered porch greets guests and offers a grand outdoor living space

A fireplace warms the cozy sitting area that is adjacent to the dining room

The bedroom enjoys a walk-in closet for easy organization

2" x 6" exterior walls available, please order plan #535-058D-0149

1 bedroom, 1 bath

Basement foundation

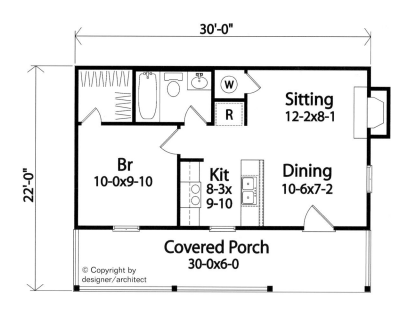

30'-0"

22'-0"

Sitting
12-2x8-1

Br
10-0x9-10

Kit
8-3x
9-10

Dining
10-6x7-2

Covered Porch
30-0x6-0

W

R

© Copyright by designer/architect

SPECIAL FEATURES

1,862 total square feet of living area

Master bedroom includes a tray ceiling, bay window, access to the patio and a private bath with oversized tub and generous closet space

Corner sink and breakfast bar faces into the breakfast area and great room

Spacious great room features a vaulted ceiling, fireplace and access to the rear patio

3 bedrooms, 2 baths, 2-car garage

Slab foundation, drawings also include crawl space foundation

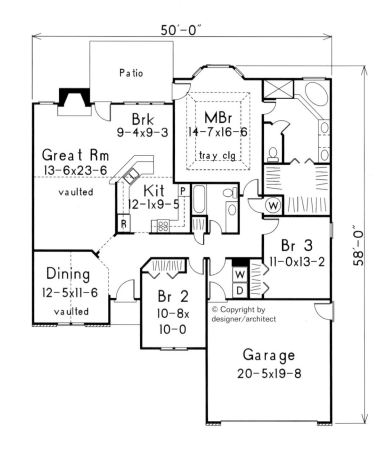

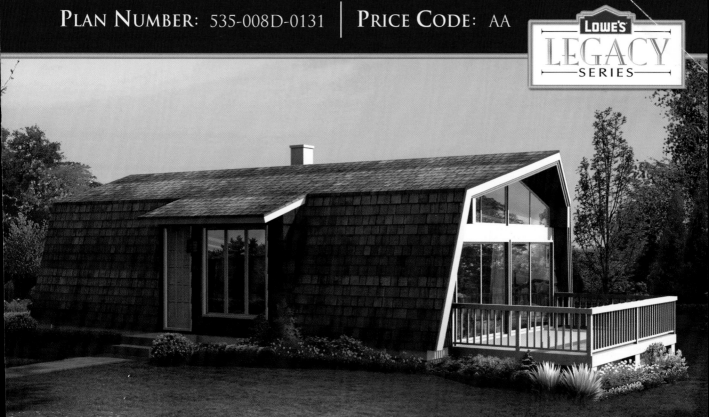

SPECIAL FEATURES

960 total square feet of living area

Interesting roof and wood beams overhang a generous-sized deck

Family room is vaulted and opens to the dining area and kitchen

Pullman-style kitchen has been skillfully designed

Two bedrooms and hall bath are located at the rear of home

2 bedrooms, 1 bath

Crawl space foundation

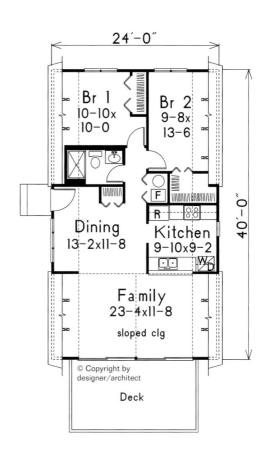

SPECIAL FEATURES

1,865 total square feet of living area

The family room, breakfast area and kitchen combine forming a large open area for family activities

A double-door entry leads to the grand master bedroom which includes two walk-in closets and a private bath

Bedrooms #2 and #3 enjoy walk-in closets and share a bath

3 bedrooms, 2 1/2 baths, 2-car garage

Basement foundation

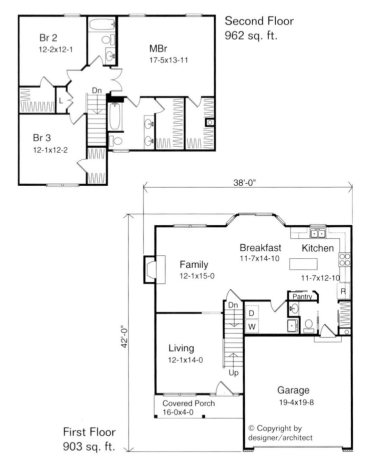

Second Floor
962 sq. ft.

Br 2
12-2x12-1

MBr
17-5x13-11

Dn

L

Br 3
12-1x12-2

First Floor
903 sq. ft.

38'-0"

42'-0"

Family
12-1x15-0

Breakfast
11-7x14-10

Kitchen
11-7x12-10

Dn

D
W

Pantry

R

Living
12-1x14-0

Up

Garage
19-4x19-8

Covered Porch
16-0x4-0

© Copyright by designer/architect

SPECIAL FEATURES

2,196 total square feet of living area

Energy efficient home with
2" x 6" exterior walls

Covered front porch leads to
the vaulted foyer which invites
guests into the great room

Master bedroom features a
walk-in closet, private bath with
double vanity, spa tub and linen closet

Large open kitchen

3 bedrooms, 2 1/2 baths, 3-car garage

Basement foundation

© Copyright by
designer/architect

SPECIAL FEATURES

750 total square feet of living area

The expansive garage features space for a washer/dryer unit and a stairway leading to the spacious apartment

The eat-in kitchen is designed for efficiency and easily opens to the wide family room

An optional laundry chute is an exciting addition to add ease to doing the laundry

1 bedroom, 1 bath, 3-car garage

Slab foundation

Second Floor
750 sq. ft.

BATH
9'-6" x 5'-0"

CLOSET
11'-4" x 3'-0"

OPTIONAL
LAUNDRY
CHUTE

EAT-IN
KITCHEN
11'-4" x 13'-0"

FAMILY ROOM
14'-0" x 18'-0"

BEDROOM
11'-4" x 11'-8"

7'-7" HIGH KNEE WALLS

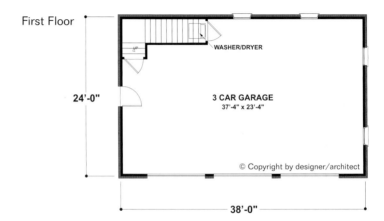

First Floor

WASHER/DRYER

24'-0"

3 CAR GARAGE
37'-4" x 23'-4"

© Copyright by designer/architect

38'-0"

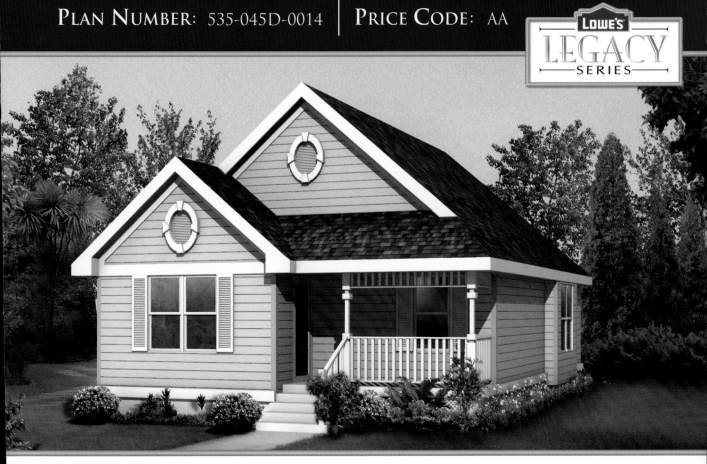

SPECIAL FEATURES

987 total square feet of living area

Galley kitchen opens into the cozy breakfast room

Convenient coat closets are located by both entrances

Dining/living room offers an expansive open area

Breakfast room has access to the outdoors

Front porch is great for enjoying outdoor living

3 bedrooms, 1 bath

Basement foundation

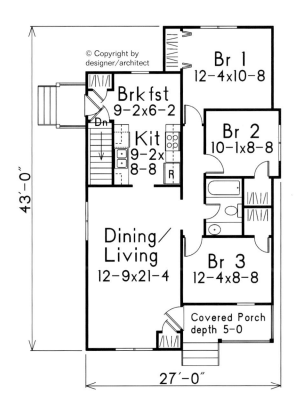

© Copyright by designer/architect

Br 1
12-4x10-8

Brk fst
9-2x6-2

Dn

Kit
9-2x
8-8

R

Br 2
10-1x8-8

43'-0"

Dining/
Living
12-9x21-4

Br 3
12-4x8-8

Covered Porch
depth 5-0

27'-0"

SPECIAL FEATURES

1,698 total square feet of living area

Kitchen includes a walk-in pantry and corner sink that faces the living area

Breakfast room is highlighted by an expanse of windows and access to the deck

Recessed foyer opens into the vaulted living room with fireplace

Master bedroom features a private bath with large walk-in closet

3 bedrooms, 2 baths, 2-car drive under garage

Basement foundation

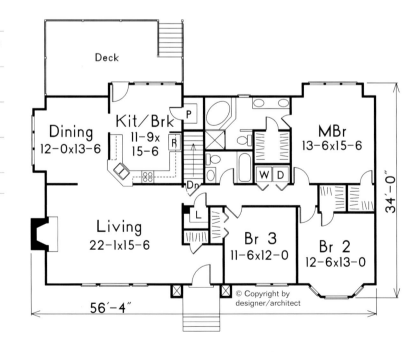

Deck

Dining
12-0x13-6

Kit/Brk
11-9x
15-6

P

R

Dn

MBr
13-6x15-6

W D

34'-0"

Living
22-1x15-6

L

Br 3
11-6x12-0

Br 2
12-6x13-0

56'-4"

© Copyright by designer/architect

LOWE'S
LEGACY
SERIES

SPECIAL FEATURES

1,635 total square feet of living area

The covered porch creates an inviting facade

A whirlpool tub and twin vanities add elegance to the master bath

The kitchen island provides extra workspace and also offers an easy way to serve buffet dinners

3 bedrooms, 2 1/2 baths, 2-car garage

Basement foundation

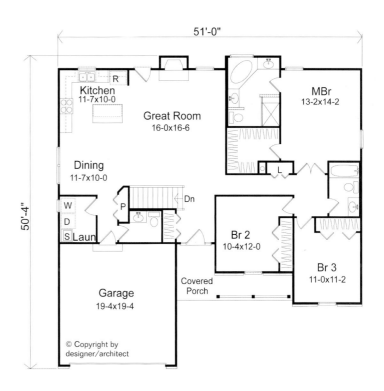

51'-0"

50'-4"

Kitchen
11-7x10-0

Great Room
16-0x16-6

MBr
13-2x14-2

Dining
11-7x10-0

Dn

Br 2
10-4x12-0

Laun

Br 3
11-0x11-2

Garage
19-4x19-4

Covered Porch

© Copyright by designer/architect

SPECIAL FEATURES

- 1,384 total square feet of living area
- The entry leads into the large vaulted family room that enjoys a corner fireplace and access to the rear yard
- The U-shaped kitchen has an abundance of counterspace and opens to the bayed dining room
- Split bedrooms ensure privacy for all
- 3 bedrooms, 2 baths, 2-car garage
- Slab foundation

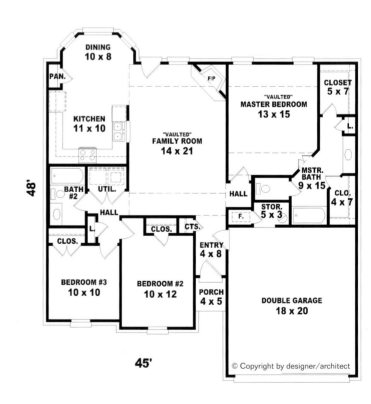

Rear View

© Copyright by designer/architect

LOWE'S LEGACY SERIES

SPECIAL FEATURES

1,858 total square feet of living area

The huge living room with fireplace
receives welcome sunlight
through a lovely bay window

Well-appointed kitchen enjoys pass-through
counters to the large dining and living rooms

Kitchen and dining room adjoin a fantastic
sunroom that accesses the deck

Spacious utility room accesses
the garage, stairs to the basement
and the entrance foyer

Master bedroom enjoys a large
bath and walk-in closet

3 bedrooms, 2 1/2 baths, 2-car garage

Basement foundation

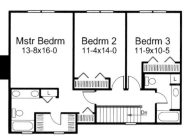

Second Floor
940 sq. ft.

Mstr Bedrm 13-8x16-0
Bedrm 2 11-4x14-0
Bedrm 3 11-9x10-5

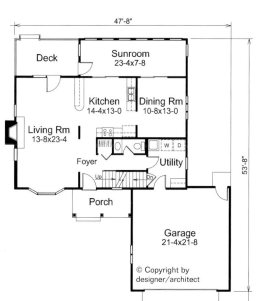

First Floor
918 sq. ft.

47'-8"

53'-8"

Deck
Sunroom 23-4x7-8
Kitchen 14-4x13-0
Dining Rm 10-8x13-0
Living Rm 13-8x23-4
Foyer
Utility
W D
Up Dn
Porch
Garage 21-4x21-8

© Copyright by
designer/architect

SPECIAL FEATURES

1,789 total square feet of living area

The relaxing master bedroom features a double-door entry, large walk-in closet and private bath with whirlpool tub

The kitchen enjoys an island with seating area and pantry

The large laundry area accesses the outdoors on both sides

3 bedrooms, 2 baths, 2-car side entry garage

Basement foundation

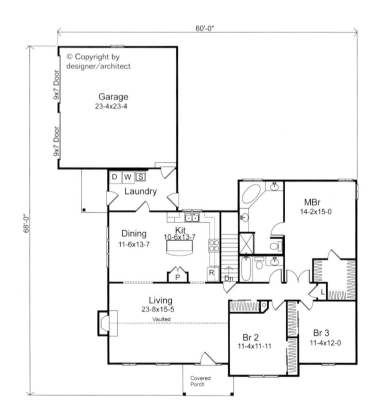

SPECIAL FEATURES

1,619 total square feet of living area

Elegant home features three quaint porches and a large rear patio

Grand-scale great room offers a dining area, fireplace with a built-in alcove and shelves for an entertainment center

First floor master bedroom has a walk-in closet, luxury bath, bay window and access to rear patio

Breakfast room with bay window contains a staircase that leads to the second floor bedrooms and loft

3 bedrooms, 2 1/2 baths, 2-car side entry garage

Basement foundation

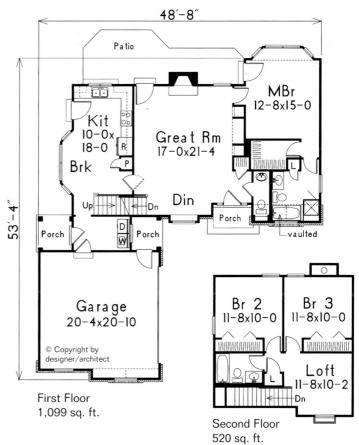

48'-8"

53'-4"

Patio

Kit
10-0x
18-0

Brk

Great Rm
17-0x21-4

MBr
12-8x15-0

Up

Dn

Din

Porch

vaulted

Porch

Porch

Garage
20-4x20-10

© Copyright by
designer/architect

First Floor
1,099 sq. ft.

Br 2
11-8x10-0

Br 3
11-8x10-0

Loft
11-8x10-2

Dn

Second Floor
520 sq. ft.

Lowe's LEGACY SERIES

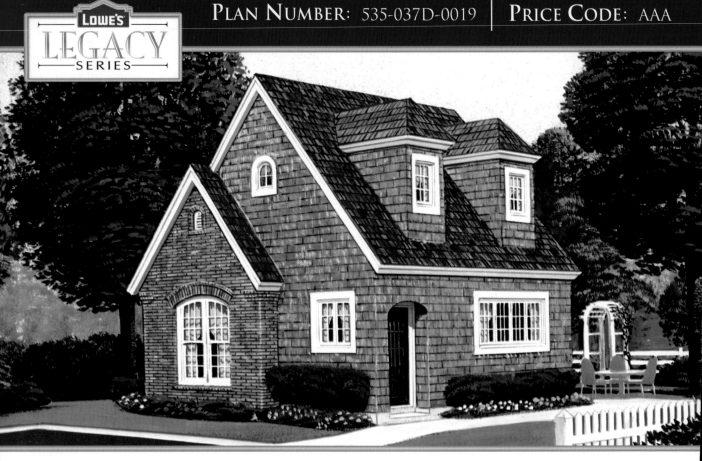

SPECIAL FEATURES

581 total square feet of living area

Kitchen/living room features space for dining and spiral steps leading to the loft area

Large loft area can easily be converted to a bedroom or home office

Entry space has a unique built-in display niche

1 bedroom, 1 bath

Slab foundation

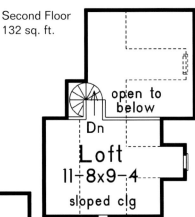

Second Floor
132 sq. ft.

open to below

Dn

Loft
11-8x9-4
sloped clg

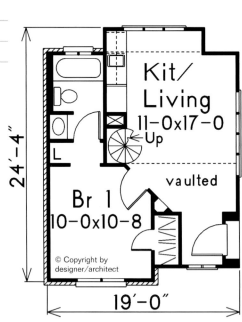

Kit/ Living
11-0x17-0
Up

vaulted

Br 1
10-0x10-8

© Copyright by designer/architect

24'-4"

19'-0"

First Floor
449 sq. ft.

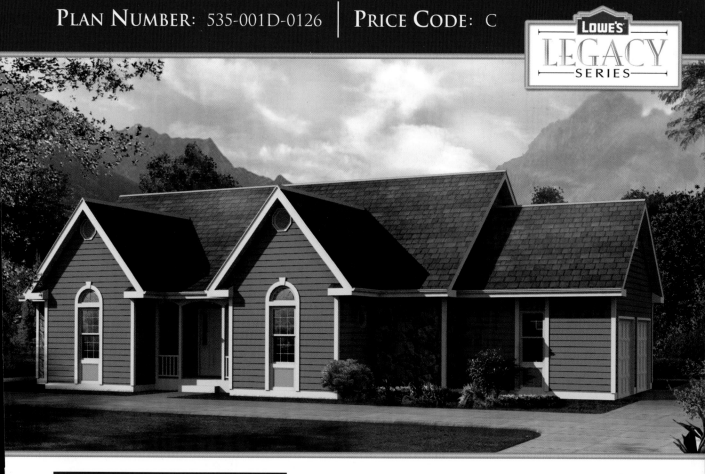

SPECIAL FEATURES

2,080 total square feet of living area

Energy efficient home with
2" x 6" exterior walls

Combined design elements
create a unique facade

Foyer leads into the large living room
with direct view to the patio

Master bedroom includes spacious
bath with garden tub, separate shower,
walk-in closet and dressing area

4 bedrooms, 2 baths, 2-car side-entry garage

Crawl space foundation, drawings also
include basement and slab foundations

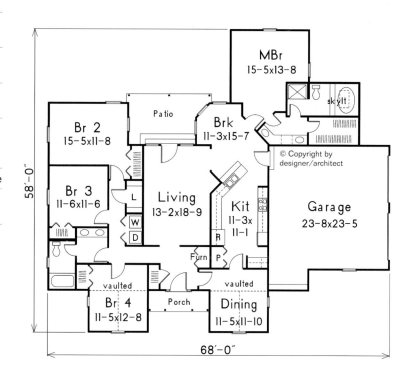

MBr
15-5x13-8

sky lt

Patio

Br 2
15-5x11-8

Brk
11-3x15-7

© Copyright by
designer/architect

Br 3
11-6x11-6

L
W
D

Living
13-2x18-9

Kit
11-3x
11-1

Garage
23-8x23-5

R

Furn

P

vaulted

vaulted

Br 4
11-5x12-8

Porch

Dining
11-5x11-10

58'-0"

68'-0"

SPECIAL FEATURES

1,500 total square feet of living area

Living room features a cathedral ceiling and opens to the breakfast room

Breakfast room has a spectacular bay window and adjoins a well-appointed kitchen with generous storage

Laundry room is convenient to the kitchen and includes a large closet

Large walk-in closet gives the master bedroom abundant storage

3 bedrooms, 2 baths, 2-car garage

Basement foundation

52'-8"

48'-0"

Patio

Breakfast
11-6x8-3

Mstr Bedrm
14-10x13-11

Living Rm
25-1x16-11
Vaulted

Kit
11-6x
11-0

R

DW

P

Entry

W   D

Porch

© Copyright by
designer/architect

Dn

Bedrm 2
10-8x13-7

Bedrm 3
10-1x12-7

Garage
21-4x21-5

LOWE'S
LEGACY
SERIES

SPECIAL FEATURES

1,153 total square feet of living area

The arched windows, detailed brickwork and roof dormer all combine to create a stylish and inviting exterior

A fireplace, U-shaped kitchen with built-in pantry and dining area with view to a side fenced patio are the many features of the living room area

The master bedroom includes a private bath, walk-in closet and access to the patio area

3 bedrooms, 2 baths, 2-car garage

Basement foundation

35'-0"

47'-8"

Bedroom #2
11-0x11-0

Master
Bedroom
12-3x13-0

Bedroom #3
11-0x9-0

Kitchen
12-3x9-2

Hall

P

Patio

DN

L

Dine

Living Room
14-8x17-10

Garage
19-4x20-4

© Copyright by
designer/architect

Entry

Porch

LEGACY
SERIES

1,477 total square feet of living area

Energy efficient home with
2" x 6" exterior walls

Oversized porch provides
protection from the elements

Innovative kitchen employs
step-saving design

Kitchen has a snack bar which opens to
the breakfast room with bay window

3 bedrooms, 2 baths, 2-car side
entry garage with storage area

Basement foundation

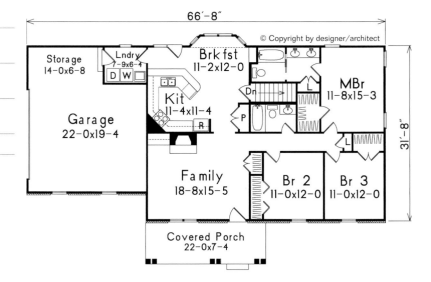

66'–8"

© Copyright by designer/architect

Storage
14-0x6-8

Lndry
7-9x6-4

D W

Brk fst
11-2x12-0

MBr
11-8x15-3

Kit
11-4x11-4

Dn

L

Garage
22-0x19-4

R

P

31'–8"

Family
18-8x15-5

Br 2
11-0x12-0

Br 3
11-0x12-0

L

Covered Porch
22-0x7-4

LOWE'S
LEGACY
SERIES

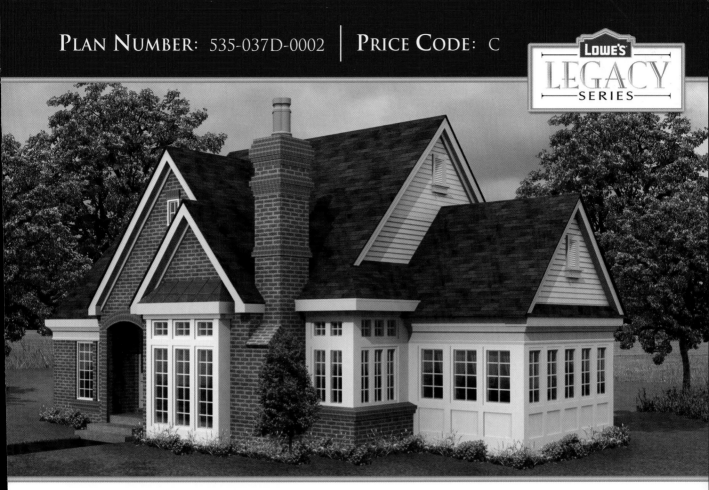

SPECIAL FEATURES

1,816 total square feet of living area

The living room features a two-way fireplace with nearby window seat

Wrap-around dining room windows create a sunroom appearance

Master bedroom has abundant closet and storage space

Rear dormers, closets and desk areas create an interesting and functional second floor

3 bedrooms, 2 1/2 baths, 2-car detached garage

Slab foundation, drawings also include crawl space foundation

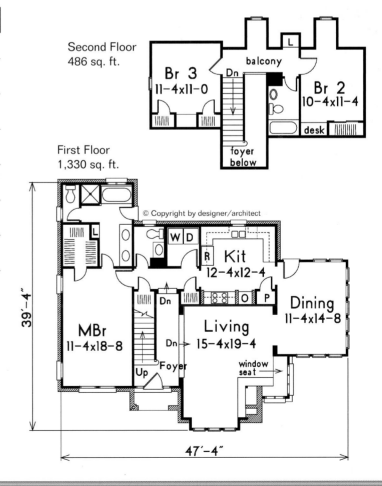

Second Floor
486 sq. ft.

Br 3
11-4x11-0

balcony

Dn

Br 2
10-4x11-4

desk

foyer
below

First Floor
1,330 sq. ft.

© Copyright by designer/architect

W D

R

Kit
12-4x12-4

Dn

O P

Dining
11-4x14-8

MBr
11-4x18-8

Dn

Living
15-4x19-4

Foyer

Up

window
seat

39'-4"

47'-4"

SPECIAL FEATURES

1,849 total square feet of living area

Energy efficient home with
2" x 6" exterior walls

The formal living room with vaulted
ceiling greets guests and offers
a dramatic first impression

The centrally located kitchen offers
a wrap-around counter opening
to the dining and family rooms for
an exceptional gathering spot

A luxurious master bedroom
pampers homeowners with a
walk-in closet and private bath
equipped with a double-bowl vanity

3 bedrooms, 2 baths, 2-car garage

Basement foundation

© Copyright by designer/architect

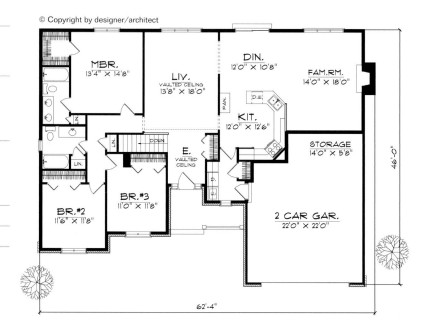

MBR.
13'4" X 14'8"

LIV.
VAULTED CEILING
13'8" X 18'0"

DIN.
12'0" X 10'8"

FAM. RM.
14'0" X 18'0"

KIT.
12'0" X 12'6"

STORAGE
14'0" X 5'8"

E.
VAULTED
CEILING

BR. #3
11'0" X 11'8"

BR. #2
11'6" X 11'8"

2 CAR GAR.
22'0" X 22'0"

46'-0"

62'-4"

SPECIAL FEATURES

1,697 total square feet of living area

Secondary bedrooms share a bath
with private dressing area

Large living room enjoys a
fireplace and vaulted ceiling

Secluded master bedroom boasts
a private deluxe bath

Open kitchen/breakfast area includes
a pantry and access to the deck

3 bedrooms, 2 baths,
2-car drive under garage

Basement foundation

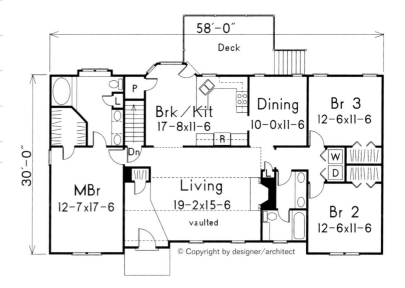

58'-0"

Deck

30'-0"

P

Brk/Kit
17-8x11-6

Dining
10-0x11-6

Br 3
12-6x11-6

Dn

R

W
D

MBr
12-7x17-6

Living
19-2x15-6
vaulted

Br 2
12-6x11-6

© Copyright by designer/architect

SPECIAL FEATURES

990 total square feet of living area

Covered front porch adds a charming feel

Vaulted ceilings in the kitchen, family and dining rooms create a spacious feel

Large linen, pantry and storage closets throughout

2 bedrooms, 1 bath

Crawl space foundation

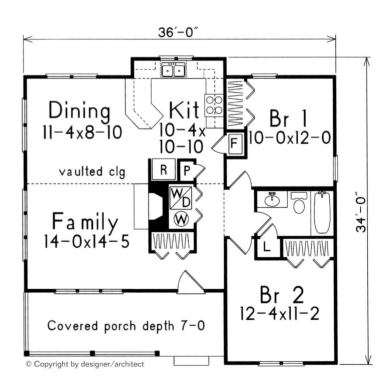

© Copyright by designer/architect

SPECIAL FEATURES

1,528 total square feet of living area

Large deck complements handsome exterior

Family room provides a welcome space for family get-togethers and includes a sloped ceiling and access to the studio and sleeping loft

Kitchen features dining space and a view to the deck

A hall bath is shared by two bedrooms on the first floor which have ample closet space

2 bedrooms, 1 bath

Crawl space foundation

Rear View

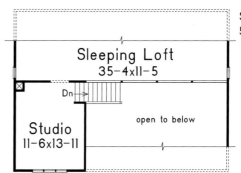

Second Floor
592 sq. ft.

Sleeping Loft
35-4x11-5

Dn

open to below

Studio
11-6x13-11

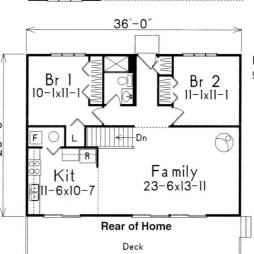

36'-0"

First Floor
936 sq. ft.

Br 1
10-1x11-1

Br 2
11-1x11-1

26'-0"

F   L

R

Dn

Kit
11-6x10-7

Family
23-6x13-11

Rear of Home

Deck

© Copyright by designer/architect

Lowe's LEGACY SERIES

SPECIAL FEATURES

1,502 total square feet of living area

The dining area or sunroom is open and airy with windows all around and includes a 9' ceiling and patio access

The kitchen features raised bars facing the dining and living rooms

The gas fireplace makes the living room a warm, friendly place to gather

3 bedrooms, 2 baths, 2-car side entry garage

Crawl space foundation, drawings also include slab foundation

Patio
17-4 x 10-10

Dining
or Sunroom
12 x 15-2
9' Ceiling

Width: 51'-8"
Depth: 51'-2"

Bedroom 1
11-6 x 13
9' Ceiling

D
W
Laun.
5-2 x 6-6

Raised Bar
DW

Master
Bedroom
16 x 12-8

Tub/ Shr

Bath

Kitchen
12 x 12

P

Clos.

Clos.

Clos.

Stor.
5-2 x 5-8

Tub/ Shr

Bath

Coat

Raised Bar

Clos.

Br. Lin.

H a l l

Living Room
17-6 x 15
(Clear)
9' Ceiling

Gas
Logs

Built-Ins

Two Car Garage
21-4 x 21-4

Bedroom 2
11-6 x 13
9' Ceiling

Front Porch
17-6 x 5-0

© Copyright by
designer/architect

SPECIAL FEATURES

1,584 total square feet of living area

Energy efficient home with
2" x 6" exterior walls

Master bedroom includes dressing
area, private bath and walk-in closet

Secondary bedrooms feature
large walk-in closets

Large living room has a patio
door to the outdoors

U-shaped kitchen features pantry, outdoor
access and convenient laundry closet

3 bedrooms, 2 baths

Crawl space foundation, drawings also
include basement and slab foundations

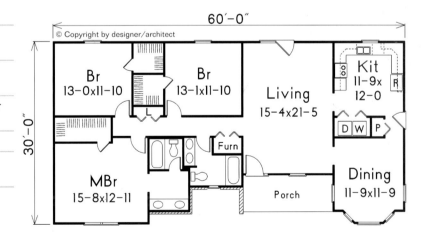

60'-0"

© Copyright by designer/architect

30'-0"

Br
13-0x11-10

Br
13-1x11-10

Living
15-4x21-5

Kit
11-9x
12-0

MBr
15-8x12-11

Furn

Porch

Dining
11-9x11-9

SPECIAL FEATURES

1,144 total square feet of living area

Energy efficient home with
2" x 6" exterior walls

A large laundry room connects the
home to the garage and contains a
sink for ease with household chores

Vaulted spaces including the kitchen,
dining and sitting rooms provide
an open atmosphere offering the
spaciousness homeowners crave

Two bedrooms share a centrally
located full bath

2 bedrooms, 1 bath, 2-car garage

Crawl space foundation

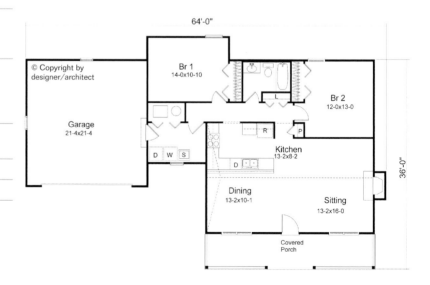

64'-0"

© Copyright by
designer/architect

Br 1
14-0x10-10

Br 2
12-0x13-0

Garage
21-4x21-4

D W S

Kitchen
13-2x8-2

R

P

L

D

36'-0"

Dining
13-2x10-1

Sitting
13-2x16-0

Covered
Porch

SPECIAL FEATURES

2,231 total square feet of living area

Open and airy L-shaped front porch leads to a spacious entrance foyer

Super-sized great room enjoys a vaulted ceiling, fireplace and opens to the breakfast room with snack bar

An abundance of cabinet storage is just one of the many features of this ideal kitchen

A luxurious first floor master bedroom has been provided along with an oversized bath and two roomy bedrooms on the second floor

3 bedrooms, 2 1/2 baths, 2-car garage

Basement foundation

Second Floor
645 sq. ft.

Attic

Br 3
13-0x17-1

open to below

Dn

Br 2
13-4x13-8

Patio

MBr
14-0x16-0

Brk
11-0x10-6

Kit
10-9x12-0

Great Rm
13-0x26-7
vaulted

Dn   Up

Laundry

D   W

Din
13-4x14-0

Entry
vaulted

Garage
19-8x20-4

© Copyright by
designer/architect

Porch depth 6-0

First Floor
1,586 sq. ft.

59'-0"

41'-0"

SPECIAL FEATURES

1,539 total square feet of living area

This two-story home is ideal for a narrow lot

The front half of the first floor consists of the combined family room, kitchen and dining area while the rear houses the master bedroom, utility and half bath

Two secondary bedrooms and a bath on the second floor round out this efficient design

3 bedrooms, 2 1/2 baths, 2-car rear entry garage

Slab foundation

View from family room

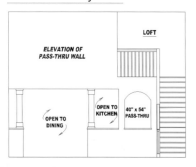

First Floor
1,108 sq. ft.

© Copyright by designer/architect

Second Floor
431 sq. ft.

SPECIAL FEATURES

1,224 total square feet of living area

Get away to this cozy A-frame featuring three bedrooms

The living and dining rooms with a free-standing fireplace walk out onto a large deck

The U-shaped kitchen is just steps away from the dining and living rooms

Both second floor bedrooms enjoy their own private balcony

3 bedrooms, 1 bath

Crawl space foundation

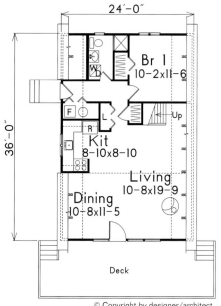

24'-0"

36'-0"

Br 1
10-2x11-6

Up

Kit
8-10x8-10

Living
10-8x19-9

Dining
10-8x11-5

Deck

© Copyright by designer/architect

First Floor
864 sq. ft.

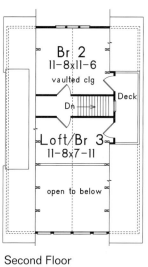

Br 2
11-8x11-6
vaulted clg

Deck

Dn

Loft/Br 3
11-8x7-11

open to below

Second Floor
360 sq. ft.

SPECIAL FEATURES

1,217 total square feet of living area

Energy efficient home with
2" x 6" exterior walls

The covered porch welcomes
guests into this lovely cottage

Inside, the massive living area includes the
combined kitchen/breakfast room and family
room, all warmed by a grand fireplace

The master bedroom enjoys a
walk-in closet and private bath

2 bedrooms, 2 baths

Basement foundation

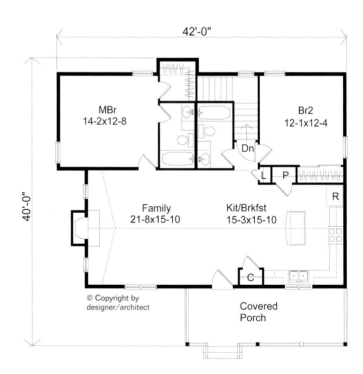

42'-0"

40'-0"

MBr
14-2x12-8

Br2
12-1x12-4

Dn

L P

R

Family
21-8x15-10

Kit/Brkfst
15-3x15-10

C

© Copyright by
designer/architect

Covered
Porch

SPECIAL FEATURES

1,558 total square feet of living area

Illuminated spaces are created by visual access to the outdoor living areas

Vaulted master bedroom features a private bath with whirlpool tub, separate shower and large walk-in closet

Convenient laundry area has garage access

Practical den or third bedroom is perfect for a variety of uses

U-shaped kitchen is adjacent to the sunny breakfast area

2 bedrooms, 2 baths, 2-car rear entry garage

Basement foundation

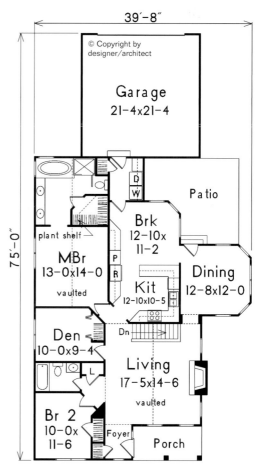

SPECIAL FEATURES

1,958 total square feet of living area

Spacious kitchen and breakfast area are open to the rear deck

A charming rail separates the family room and breakfast area keeping an open feel

Dormers add interest and spaciousness in bedroom #2

Bonus room on the second floor is included in the square footage

3 bedrooms, 2 1/2 baths, 2-car side entry garage

Basement foundation, drawings also include slab and crawl space foundations

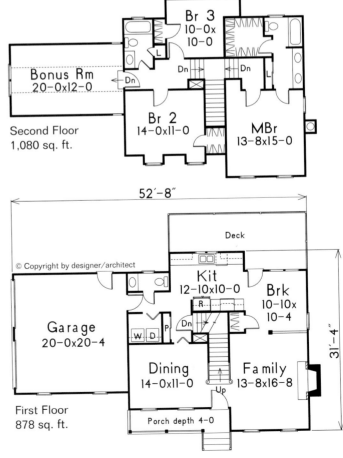

Br 3
10-0x 10-0

Bonus Rm
20-0x12-0

Br 2
14-0x11-0

MBr
13-8x15-0

Second Floor
1,080 sq. ft.

52'-8"

Deck

Kit
12-10x10-0

Brk
10-10x 10-4

© Copyright by designer/architect

Garage
20-0x20-4

Dining
14-0x11-0

Family
13-8x16-8

31'-4"

First Floor
878 sq. ft.

Porch depth 4-0

SPECIAL FEATURES

1,680 total square feet of living area

Highly functional lower level includes a wet hall with storage, laundry area, workshop and cozy ski lounge with an enormous fireplace

First floor is warmed by a large fireplace in the living/dining area which features a spacious wrap-around deck

Lots of sleeping space for guests or a large family

5 bedrooms, 2 1/2 baths

Walk-out basement foundation

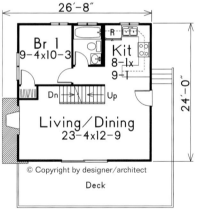

26'-8"

Br 1
9-4x10-3

Kit
8-1x
9-1

R

Dn   Up

Living/Dining
23-4x12-9

24'-0"

© Copyright by designer/architect

Deck

First Floor
576 sq. ft.

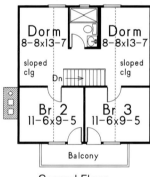

Dorm
8-8x13-7
sloped clg

Dorm
8-8x13-7
sloped clg

Dn

Br 2
11-6x9-5

Br 3
11-6x9-5

Balcony

Second Floor
528 sq. ft.

Workshop
13-4x9-7

D W

F

Up

Ski Lounge
14-1x12-9

Wet Hall

Lower Level
576 sq. ft.

SPECIAL FEATURES

1,240 total square feet of living area

Kitchen/breakfast area combine for added spaciousness

Sloped ceiling adds appeal in the sitting area

The utilities are located on the first floor near the garage

2 bedrooms, 1 bath, 2-car garage

Basement foundation

Second Floor
1,240 sq. ft.

First Floor

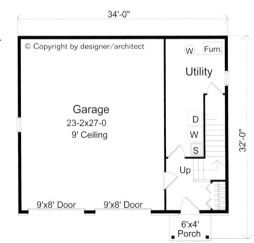

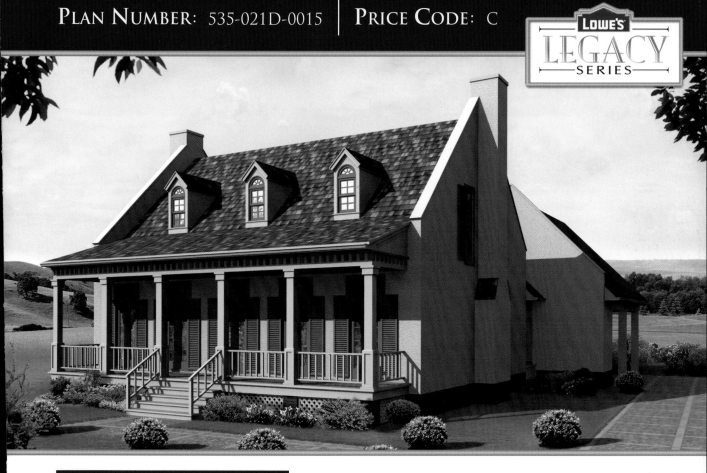

SPECIAL FEATURES

1,700 total square feet of living area

Energy efficient home with
2" x 6" exterior walls

Fully appointed kitchen with wet bar

Linen drop from the second floor bath
to the utility room is a handy feature

Master bath includes raised marble
tub and a sloped ceiling

3 bedrooms, 2 1/2 baths,
2-car attached carport

Crawl space foundation, drawings also
include basement and slab foundations

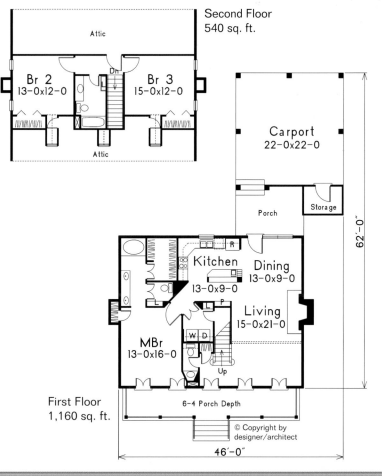

Second Floor
540 sq. ft.

First Floor
1,160 sq. ft.

© Copyright by
designer/architect

LEGACY SERIES

SPECIAL FEATURES

1,817 total square feet of living area

Energy efficient home with
2" x 6" exterior walls

12' ceilings grace the entry and
connecting great room

The formal dining room boasts a
12' ceiling and a wall of windows
bringing in warm natural light

The bayed nook accesses the outdoors
through sliding glass doors

The secluded master bedroom features
two closets and a private bath with
whirlpool tub and double-bowl vanity

3 bedrooms, 2 baths, 2-car garage

Basement foundation

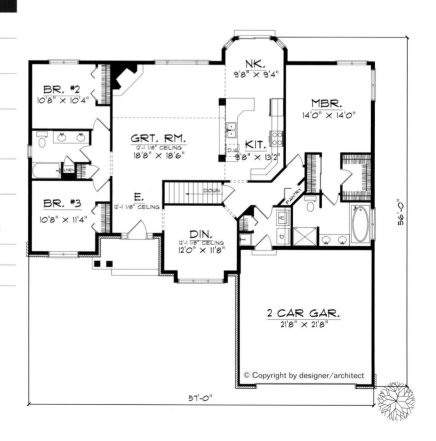

NK.
9'8" x 9'4"

MBR.
14'0" x 14'0"

BR. #2
10'8" x 10'4"

GRT. RM.
12'-1 1/8" CEILING
18'8" x 18'6"

KIT.
9'8" x 13'2"

DOWN

BR. #3
10'8" x 11'4"

E.
12'-1 1/8" CEILING

PANTRY

DIN.
12'-1 1/8" CEILING
12'0" x 11'8"

2 CAR GAR.
21'8" x 21'8"

56'-0"

57'-0"

© Copyright by designer/architect

150

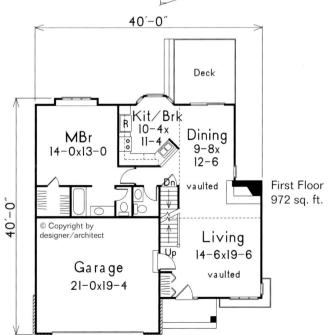

SPECIAL FEATURES

1,448 total square feet of living area

Dining room conveniently adjoins kitchen and accesses rear deck

Private first floor master bedroom

Secondary bedrooms share a bath and cozy loft area

3 bedrooms, 2 1/2 baths, 2-car garage

Basement foundation

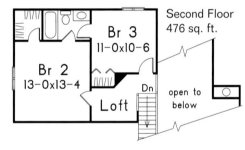

Second Floor
476 sq. ft.

Br 3
11-0x10-6

Br 2
13-0x13-4

Loft

Dn

open to below

40'-0"

40'-0"

Deck

Kit/Brk
10-4x
11-4

Dining
9-8x
12-6

MBr
14-0x13-0

Dn   vaulted

First Floor
972 sq. ft.

© Copyright by designer/architect

Living
14-6x19-6

Up   vaulted

Garage
21-0x19-4

SPECIAL FEATURES

1,567 total square feet of living area

Front gables and extended porch
add charm to the facade

Large bay windows add brightness
to the breakfast and dining rooms

The master bath boasts an oversized
tub, separate shower, double
sinks and large walk-in closet

Living room features a vaulted
ceiling and a prominent fireplace

3 bedrooms, 2 baths,
2-car drive under garage

Basement foundation

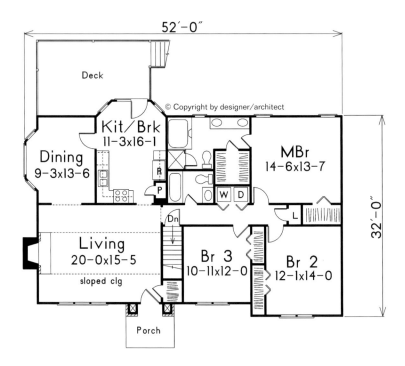

52'-0"

Deck

© Copyright by designer/architect

Kit/Brk
11-3x16-1

Dining
9-3x13-6

MBr
14-6x13-7

R

P

W D

Dn

L

32'-0"

Living
20-0x15-5

sloped clg

Br 3
10-11x12-0

Br 2
12-1x14-0

Porch

SPECIAL FEATURES

1,082 total square feet of living area

A convenient coat closet is located just inside the entryway

The large living room offers an optional double-door entry into the den

Extremely functional kitchen leads to the dining room with sliding glass doors opening onto the rear patio

Nice-sized bedrooms enjoy plenty of large closet space

3 bedrooms, 1 bath, 2-car garage

Basement foundation, drawings also include crawl space foundation

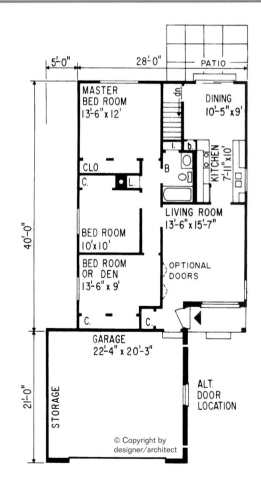

Lowe's
LEGACY
SERIES

SPECIAL FEATURES

868 total square feet of living area

Large windows brighten the adjoining dining and great rooms

The efficient kitchen includes a snack bar counter connecting to the dining room

A linen closet and utility room provide essential storage space

1 bedroom, 1 bath, 2-car garage

Basement foundation

Second Floor
868 sq. ft.

Dining
13x10-4

Kitchen

Great Room
13x11

MBr.
12x10-9

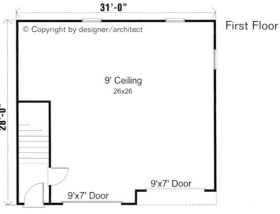

31'-0"

© Copyright by designer/architect

First Floor

9' Ceiling
26x26

28'-0"

9'x7' Door

9'x7' Door

LOWE'S
LEGACY
SERIES

SPECIAL FEATURES

950 total square feet of living area

The deck is attached to the kitchen, perfect for outdoor dining

Vaulted ceiling, open stairway and fireplace complement the great room

Bedroom #2 with a sloped ceiling and box-bay window can convert to a den

Master bedroom has a walk-in closet, plant shelf, separate dressing area and private access to the bath

Kitchen has garage access and opens to the great room

2 bedrooms, 1 bath, 1-car garage

Basement foundation

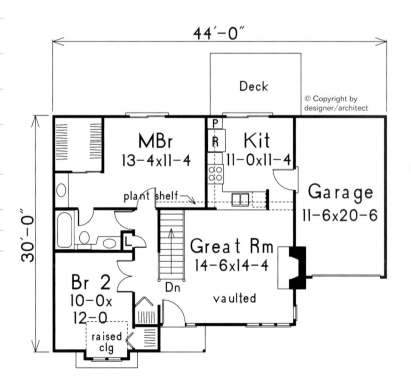

44'-0"

Deck

© Copyright by designer/architect

30'-0"

MBr
13-4x11-4

Kit
11-0x11-4

P
R

Garage
11-6x20-6

plant shelf

Great Rm
14-6x14-4

Dn

vaulted

Br 2
10-0x
12-0

raised clg

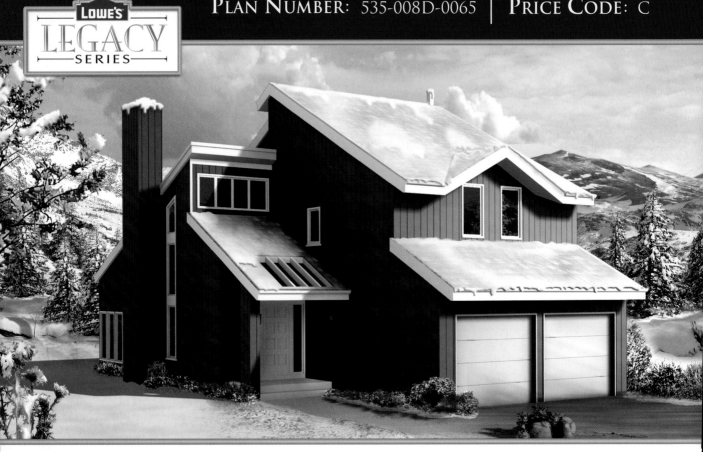

SPECIAL FEATURES

1,873 total square feet of living area

Interesting contemporary roof lines

Vaulted living room is separated from foyer by glass block wall

Spacious sun room with skylights adjoins living room

Kitchen has a useful breakfast bar

Master bedroom has all the pleasing amenities including a balcony

3 bedrooms, 2 1/2 baths, 2-car garage

Basement foundation, drawings also include slab foundation and partial basement/crawl space foundation

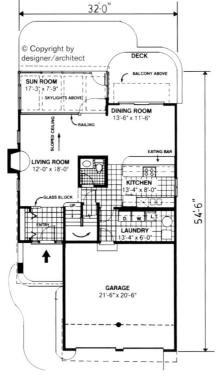

First Floor
896 sq. ft.

Second Floor
977 sq. ft.

SPECIAL FEATURES

1,978 total square feet of living area

Master bedroom includes a
walk-in closet and private full bath

Entry opens into the large living area with
bay window, fireplace and plant shelf

Open kitchen and dining area
includes a bar and access to deck

4 bedrooms, 3 baths,
2-car drive under garage

Partial basement/slab foundation

© Copyright by designer/architect

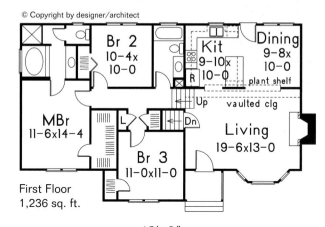

First Floor
1,236 sq. ft.

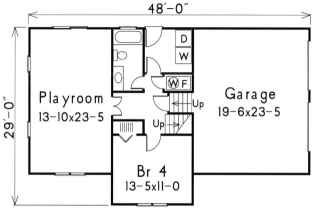

Lower Level
742 sq. ft.

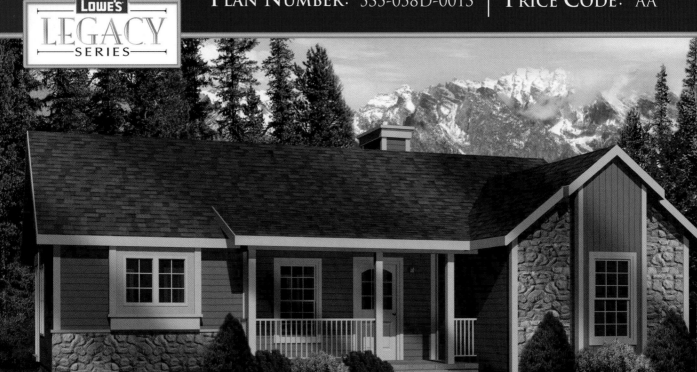

SPECIAL FEATURES

1,073 total square feet of living area

Home includes a lovely covered front porch and a screened porch off the dining area

Attractive box window brightens the kitchen

Space for an efficiency washer and dryer is located conveniently between the bedrooms

Family room is spotlighted by a fireplace with flanking bookshelves and spacious vaulted ceiling

2 bedrooms, 1 bath

Crawl space foundation

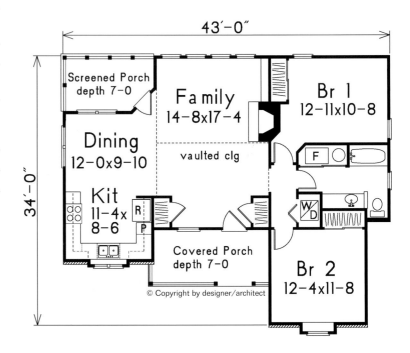

© Copyright by designer/architect

SPECIAL FEATURES

496 total square feet of living area

The traditional front exterior and rear both enjoy shady porches for relaxing evenings

The living room with bayed dining area is open to a functional L-shaped kitchen with a convenient pantry

A full bath, large walk-in closet and access to both the rear porch and the garage enhance the spacious bedroom

1 bedroom, 1 bath, 2-car garage

Slab foundation

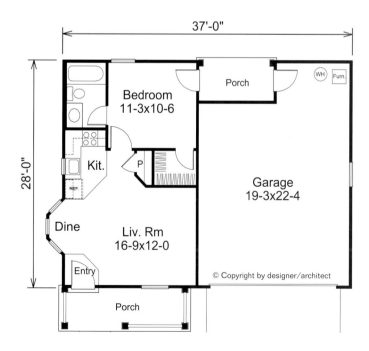

37'-0"

28'-0"

Bedroom
11-3x10-6

Porch

WH   Furn.

Kit.

P

Garage
19-3x22-4

Dine

Liv. Rm
16-9x12-0

Entry

© Copyright by designer/architect

Porch

SPECIAL FEATURES

2,155 total square feet of living area

Delightful family room embraces both the front and rear including a cozy fireplace and stairs to a studio above the garage

An L-shaped kitchen to the rear, enjoys a bay window

Compartmented bath and large walk-in closet are just a few great features of the master bedroom

Optional studio above garage has an additional 349 square feet of living area

4 bedrooms, 3 baths, 2-car garage

Partial basement/crawl space foundation, drawings also include crawl space and slab foundations

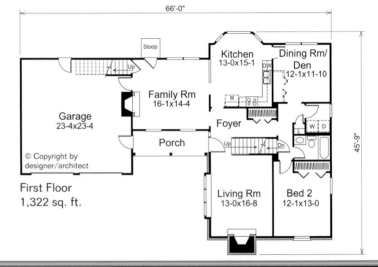

Studio
13-5x23-4

Master Bed
13-7x18-0

Bed 2
10-0x13-4

Bed 3
10-1x10-10

Second Floor
833 sq. ft.

66'-0"

Stoop

Kitchen
13-0x15-1

Dining Rm/
Den
12-1x11-10

Family Rm
16-1x14-4

Garage
23-4x23-4

Foyer

Porch

© Copyright by
designer/architect

45'-9"

Living Rm
13-0x16-8

Bed 2
12-1x13-0

First Floor
1,322 sq. ft.

SPECIAL FEATURES

1,624 total square feet of living area

Master bedroom has a private
entry from the outdoors

Garage is adjacent to the utility room
with convenient storage closet

Large family and dining areas feature
a fireplace and porch access

Pass-through kitchen opens directly
to the cozy breakfast area

3 bedrooms, 2 baths, 2-car side entry garage

Basement foundation, drawings also
include crawl space and slab foundations

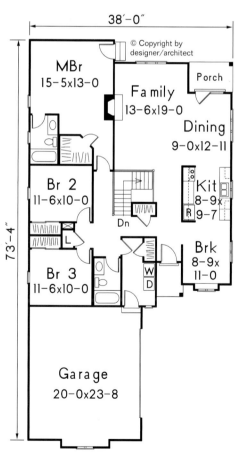

38'-0"

© Copyright by
designer/architect

MBr
15-5x13-0

Family
13-6x19-0

Porch

Dining
9-0x12-11

Br 2
11-6x10-0

Kit
8-9x
9-7

R

73'-4"

Dn

L

Brk
8-9x
11-0

Br 3
11-6x10-0

W
D

Garage
20-0x23-8

LOWE'S
LEGACY
SERIES

SPECIAL FEATURES

1,480 total square feet of living area

Sliding glass doors on the expansive deck lead to a spacious dining/living area that is sure to be a great gathering place

A vaulted balcony on the second floor could provide extra sleeping space or a secluded home office

The U-shaped kitchen is functional and keeps everything within reach

3 bedrooms, 2 baths, 1-car garage

Basement foundation

First Floor
994 sq. ft.

Lower Level

Second Floor
486 sq. ft.

© Copyright by
designer/architect

LOWE'S **LEGACY** SERIES

SPECIAL FEATURES

2,179 total square feet of living area

Open floor plan and minimal halls eliminate wasted space and create efficiency

First floor master bedroom is conveniently located near the large kitchen

Three bedrooms on the second floor share a large bath and nearby linen closet

2" x 6" exterior walls available, please order plan #535-058D-0088

4 bedrooms, 2 1/2 baths, 2-car garage

Basement foundation

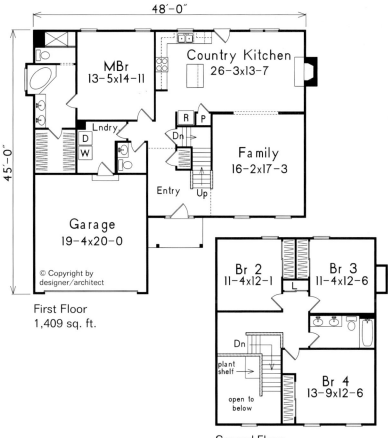

First Floor
1,409 sq. ft.

Second Floor
770 sq. ft.

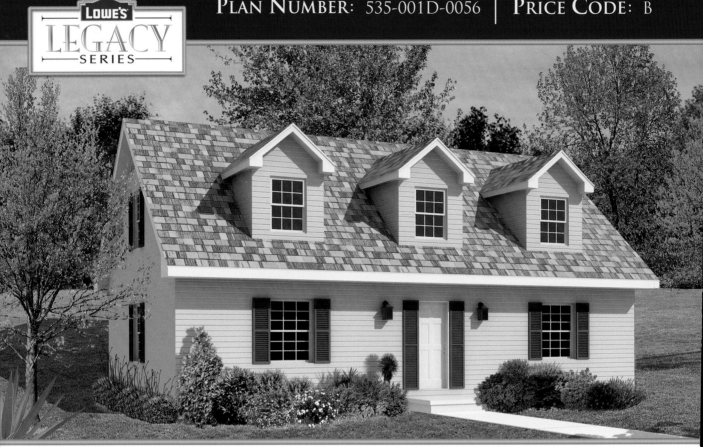

SPECIAL FEATURES

1,705 total square feet of living area

Cozy design includes two bedrooms on the first floor and two bedrooms on the second floor for added privacy

L-shaped kitchen provides easy access to the dining room and the outdoors

Convenient first floor laundry area

2" x 6" exterior walls available, please order plan #535-001D-0111

4 bedrooms, 2 baths

Crawl space foundation, drawings also include basement and slab foundations

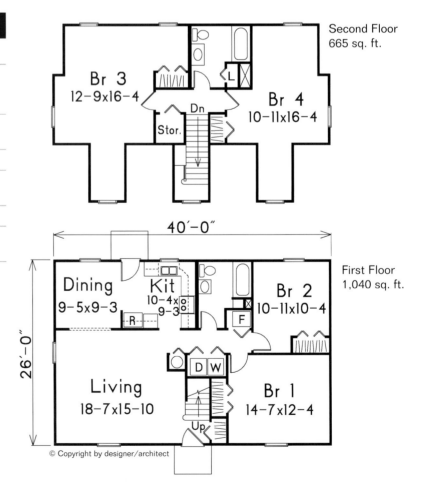

Second Floor
665 sq. ft.

Br 3
12-9x16-4

Dn

Stor.

Br 4
10-11x16-4

40'-0"

First Floor
1,040 sq. ft.

26'-0"

Dining
9-5x9-3

Kit
10-4x
9-3

R

Br 2
10-11x10-4

F

D W

Living
18-7x15-10

Br 1
14-7x12-4

Up

© Copyright by designer/architect

SPECIAL FEATURES

2,077 total square feet of living area

Two sets of French doors provide access to the rear yard and a covered porch offers a relaxing hideaway

The great room shares the fireplace with the adjoining dining area and kitchen

Bonus room on the second floor has an additional 211 square feet of living area

4 bedrooms, 2 1/2 baths, 2-car garage

Basement foundation

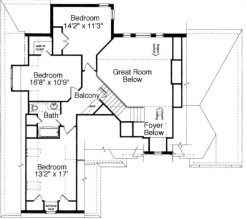

Second Floor
545 sq. ft.

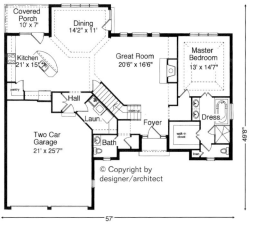

First Floor
1,532 sq. ft.

© Copyright by designer/architect

SPECIAL FEATURES

1,106 total square feet of living area

Delightful A-frame provides exciting vacation-style living all year long

Deck accesses a large living room with an open soaring ceiling

Enormous sleeping area is provided on the second floor with balcony overlook to living room below

2 bedrooms, 1 bath

Pier foundation

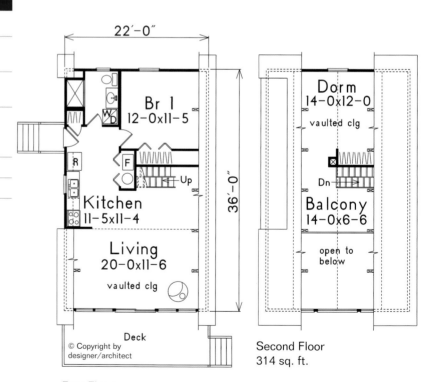

22'-0"

36'-0"

Br 1
12-0x11-5

Kitchen
11-5x11-4

Living
20-0x11-6

vaulted clg

Up

F

R

© Copyright by
designer/architect

Deck

First Floor
792 sq. ft.

Dorm
14-0x12-0

vaulted clg

Dn

Balcony
14-0x6-6

open to
below

Second Floor
314 sq. ft.

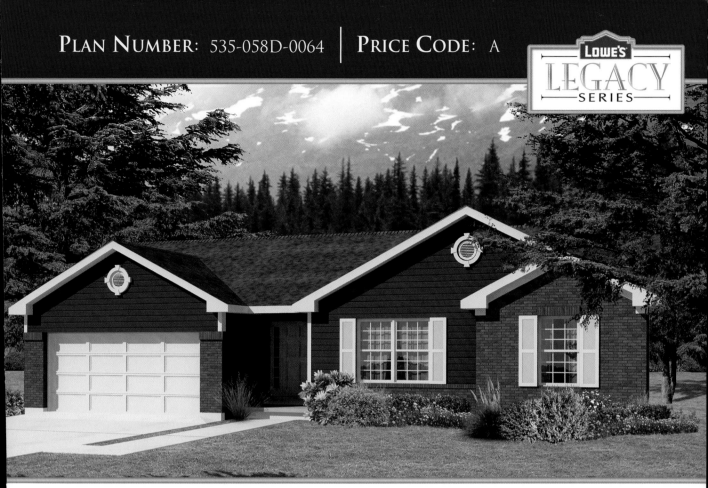

LOWE'S LEGACY SERIES

SPECIAL FEATURES

1,323 total square feet of living area

The vaulted family room provides an elegant first impression

The master bedroom enjoys a walk-in closet and private bath

The kitchen connects to the breakfast area which includes access to the outdoors

3 bedrooms, 2 baths, 2-car garage

Basement foundation

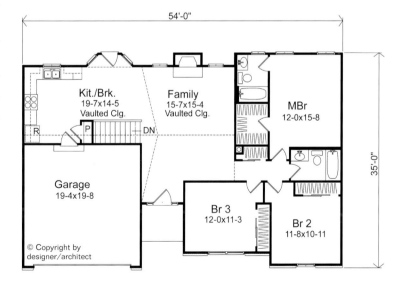

54'-0"

35'-0"

Kit./Brk.
19-7x14-5
Vaulted Clg.

Family
15-7x15-4
Vaulted Clg.

MBr
12-0x15-8

R   P   DN

Garage
19-4x19-8

© Copyright by designer/architect

Br 3
12-0x11-3

Br 2
11-8x10-11

SPECIAL FEATURES

1,020 total square feet of living area

Kitchen features open stairs, pass-through to great room, pantry and deck access

Master bedroom features private entrance to bath, large walk-in closet and sliding doors to deck

Informal entrance into home through the garage

Great room has a vaulted ceiling and fireplace

2 bedrooms, 1 bath, 2-car garage

Basement foundation

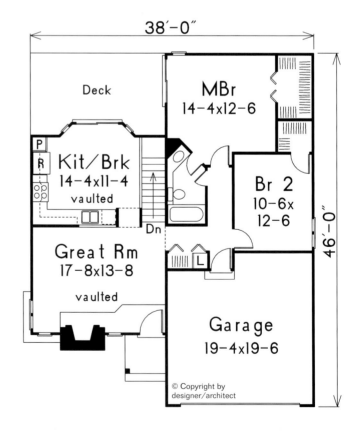

Special Features

1,785 total square feet of living area

Energy efficient home with
2" x 6" exterior walls

A see-through fireplace warms the
great room and kitchen/dining area

The kitchen provides an abundance of
counterspace and includes a center island

A convenient laundry area located
off the kitchen and garage features
a coat closet and half bath

The bedrooms are located away from
the main living areas for privacy

3 bedrooms, 2 1/2 baths, 2-car garage

Basement foundation

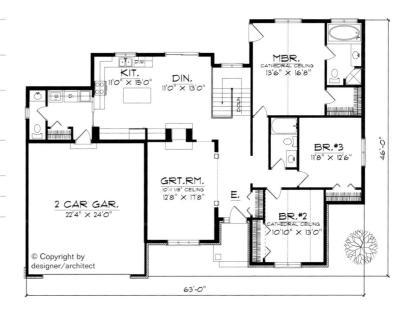

© Copyright by
designer/architect

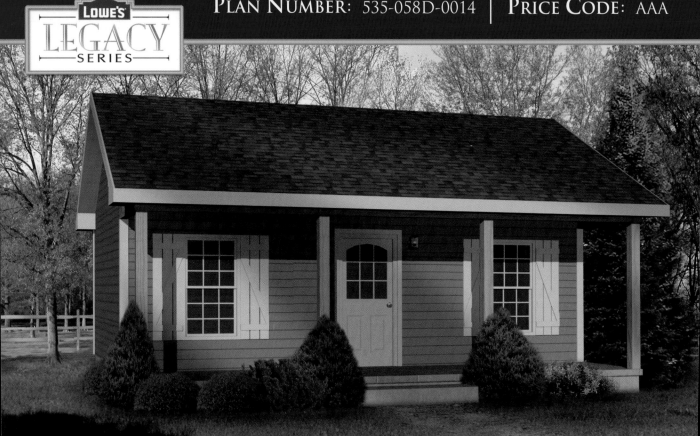

SPECIAL FEATURES

416 total square feet of living area

Open floor plan creates a spacious feeling

Covered porch has rustic appeal

The kitchen offers plenty of cabinets and workspace

Large linen closet is centrally located and close to the bath

2" x 6" exterior walls available, please order plan #535-058D-0076

Sleeping area, 1 bath

Slab foundation

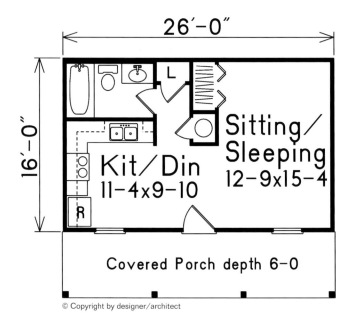

26'-0"

16'-0"

Sitting/Sleeping
12-9x15-4

Kit/Din
11-4x9-10

L

R

Covered Porch depth 6-0

© Copyright by designer/architect

SPECIAL FEATURES

960 total square feet of living area

Charming L-shaped kitchen offers lots of space, a cheery dining area and glass sliding doors to the patio

Convenient to the kitchen is a spacious laundry room and stairway to the basement

All bedrooms enjoy ample closet storage

Handy service door is provided in front of the garage

3 bedrooms, 1 bath, 2-car garage

Basement foundation, drawings also include crawl space and slab foundations

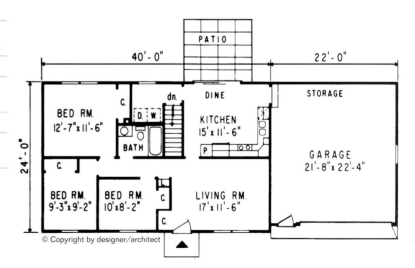

© Copyright by designer/architect

SPECIAL FEATURES

1,551 total square feet of living area

A centrally located kitchen is able to
effortlessly serve the formal dining
room and casual breakfast area

Four spacious bedrooms offer
space for a large family

The rear of the home includes an essential
storage room accessed from the rear yard

4 bedrooms, 2 baths

Slab foundation

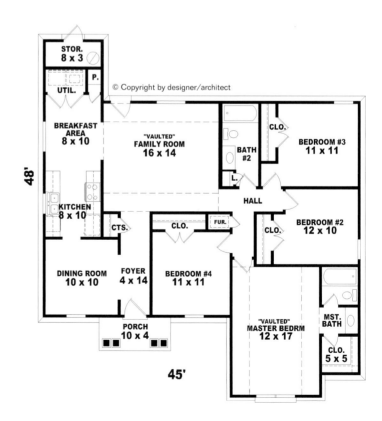

STOR.
8 x 3

UTIL.   P.

© Copyright by designer/architect

BREAKFAST
AREA
8 x 10

"VAULTED"
FAMILY ROOM
16 x 14

BATH
#2

CLO.

BEDROOM #3
11 x 11

48'

KITCHEN
8 x 10

CTS.

CLO.   FUR.

HALL

CLO.

BEDROOM #2
12 x 10

DINING ROOM
10 x 10

FOYER
4 x 14

BEDROOM #4
11 x 11

PORCH
10 x 4

"VAULTED"
MASTER BEDRM
12 x 17

MST.
BATH

CLO.
5 x 5

45'

SPECIAL FEATURES

1,954 total square feet of living area

Energy efficient home with
2" x 6" exterior walls

Living and dining areas include vaulted
ceilings and combine for added openness

Convenient access to laundry
room from garage

Appealing bay window in family
room attracts light

Raised whirlpool tub featured in master bath

3 bedrooms, 2 1/2 baths, 2-car garage

Basement foundation

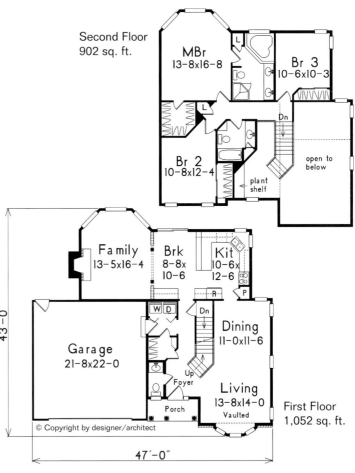

Second Floor
902 sq. ft.

MBr
13-8x16-8

Br 3
10-6x10-3

Br 2
10-8x12-4

Dn

open to
below

plant
shelf

First Floor
1,052 sq. ft.

Family
13-5x16-4

Brk
8-8x
10-6

Kit
10-6x
12-6

W D

Garage
21-8x22-0

Dn

Dining
11-0x11-6

Up

Foyer

Living
13-8x14-0
Vaulted

Porch

43'-0"

47'-0"

© Copyright by designer/architect

SPECIAL FEATURES

1,800 total square feet of living area

Energy efficient home with
2" x 6" exterior walls

The garage includes stair
access to the lower level

The living room boasts a tray ceiling,
fireplace, built-in cabinets and French
doors which open to the outdoors

Kitchen has a snack
bar/island for extra seating

3 bedrooms, 2 1/2 baths,
3-car side entry garage

Basement foundation

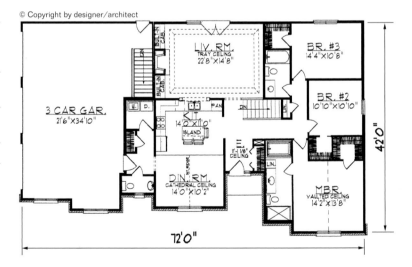

© Copyright by designer/architect

LIV. RM.
TRAY CEILING
22'8"X14'8"

BR. #3
14'4"X10'8"

3 CAR GAR.
21'6"X34'10"

KIT.
14'0"X11'0"
ISLAND

BR. #2
10'10"X10'10"

PAN.

11'-1 1/8"
CEILING

DIN. RM.
CATHEDRAL CEILING
14'0"X10'2"

MBR
VAULTED CEILING
14'2"X13'8"

42'0"

72'0"

SPECIAL FEATURES

1,512 total square feet of living area

The spacious family room is warmed by a grand fireplace

The kitchen/breakfast area features a pantry and access to the outdoors

The laundry area includes space for an optional sink

All bedrooms are located on the second floor for privacy

3 bedrooms, 2 1/2 baths, 2-car garage

Basement foundation

Second Floor
777 sq. ft.

Br 2
10-0x12-0

Br 3
10-0x12-0

Dn

MBr
15-1x11-3
Vaulted Clg.

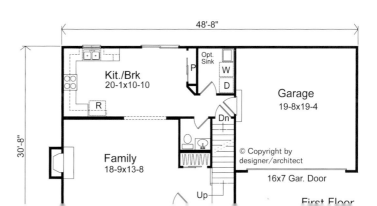

48'-8"

30'-8"

Opt. Sink

Kit./Brk
20-1x10-10

P

W

D

R

Garage
19-8x19-4

Dn

© Copyright by designer/architect

Family
18-9x13-8

16x7 Gar. Door

Up

First Floor

LOWE'S LEGACY SERIES

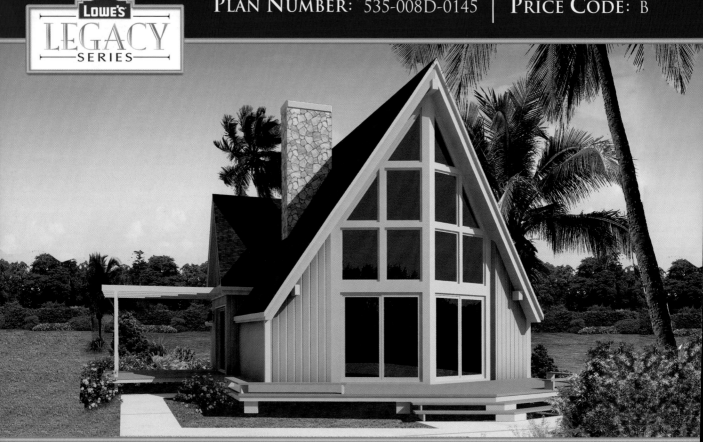

SPECIAL FEATURES

1,750 total square feet of living area

The family room is brightened by floor-to-ceiling windows and sliding doors providing access to a large deck

Second floor sitting area is perfect for a game room or entertaining

Kitchen includes eat-in dining area plus outdoor dining patio as a bonus

Plenty of closet and storage space throughout

3 bedrooms, 2 baths

Basement foundation, drawings also include crawl space and slab foundations

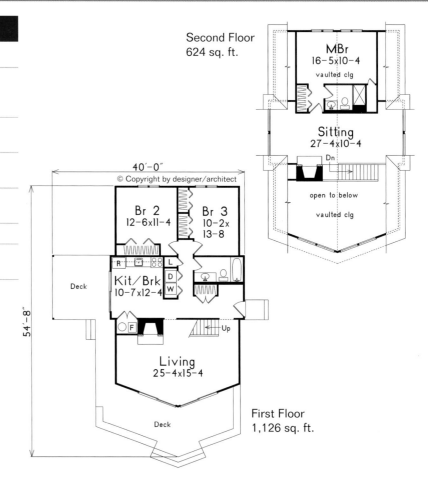

Second Floor
624 sq. ft.

MBr
16-5x10-4
vaulted clg

Sitting
27-4x10-4

Dn

open to below

vaulted clg

40'-0"

© Copyright by designer/architect

Br 2
12-6x11-4

Br 3
10-2x
13-8

Kit/Brk
10-7x12-4

Deck

54'-8"

F

Up

Living
25-4x15-4

Deck

First Floor
1,126 sq. ft.

LOWE'S
LEGACY
SERIES

SPECIAL FEATURES

1,664 total square feet of living area

Energy efficient home with
2" x 6" exterior walls

L-shaped country kitchen includes
pantry and cozy breakfast area

Bedrooms are located on the
second floor for privacy

Master bedroom includes walk-in
closet, dressing area and bath

3 bedrooms, 2 1/2 baths, 2-car garage

Crawl space foundation, drawings also
include basement and slab foundations

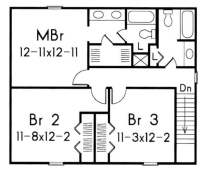

MBr
12-11x12-11

Br 2
11-8x12-2

Br 3
11-3x12-2

Dn

Second Floor
832 sq. ft.

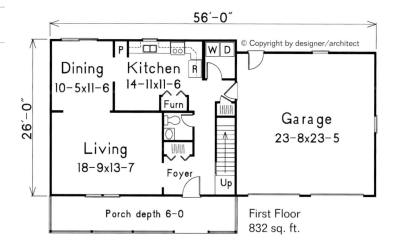

56'-0"

26'-0"

© Copyright by designer/architect

P

Dining
10-5x11-6

Kitchen
14-11x11-6

W D

R

Furn

Living
18-9x13-7

Foyer

Up

Garage
23-8x23-5

Porch depth 6-0

First Floor
832 sq. ft.

LOWE'S LEGACY SERIES

SPECIAL FEATURES

2,106 total square feet of living area

Energy efficient home with
2" x 6" exterior walls

9' ceilings throughout home

Large two-story foyer features
open staircase and plant ledge

Kitchen with centrally located eating bar
offers double pantries for additional storage

An arch with columns on either side
separates dining and living rooms

Master bath includes plush dressing area,
double sinks, a spa tub, linen cabinet and
a separate room with toilet and shower

3 bedrooms, 2 1/2 baths, 2-car garage

Basement foundation

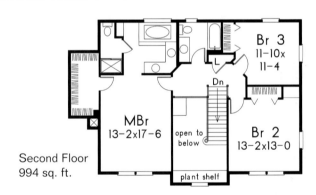

Second Floor
994 sq. ft.

Br 3
11-10x
11-4

Dn

L

MBr
13-2x17-6

open to
below

Br 2
13-2x13-0

plant shelf

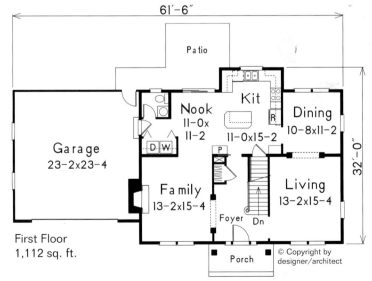

61'-6"

Patio

Kit

Nook
11-0x
11-2

11-0x15-2

Dining
10-8x11-2

R

D W

P

32'-0"

Garage
23-2x23-4

Family
13-2x15-4

Living
13-2x15-4

Foyer

Dn

First Floor
1,112 sq. ft.

Porch

LOWE'S
LEGACY
SERIES

SPECIAL FEATURES

1,443 total square feet of living area

A raised foyer and a cathedral ceiling in the living room add character to the interior

Impressive tall-wall fireplace between the living and dining rooms

Open U-shaped kitchen features a cheerful breakfast bay

Angular side deck accentuates patio and garden

First floor master bedroom has a walk-in closet and a corner window

3 bedrooms, 2 baths, 2-car garage

Basement foundation

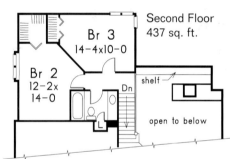

Second Floor
437 sq. ft.

Br 3
14-4x10-0

Br 2
12-2x
14-0

shelf

Dn

open to below

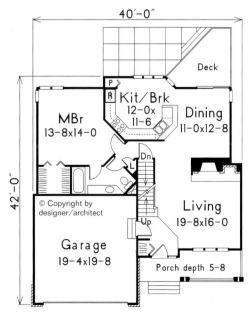

40'-0"

First Floor
1,006 sq. ft.

Deck

P
R

Kit/Brk
12-0x
11-6

Dining
11-0x12-8

MBr
13-8x14-0

Dn

© Copyright by
designer/architect

Living
19-8x16-0

42'-0"

Up

Garage
19-4x19-8

Porch depth 5-8

SPECIAL FEATURES

2,045 total square feet of living area

Master bedroom includes a
walk-in closet and private bath with
corner tub and separate shower

Both the family and breakfast
rooms access the outdoors

Two-story foyer with attractive transom
windows opens into the formal living room

3 bedrooms, 2 1/2 baths, 2-car garage

Basement foundation

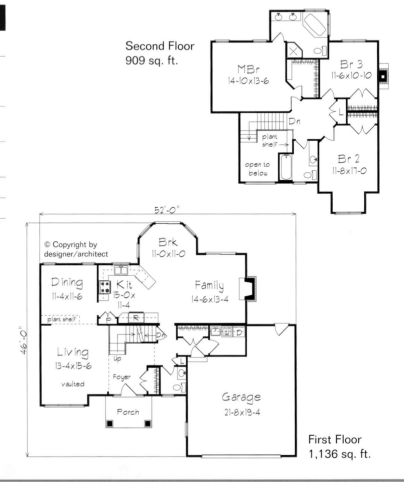

Second Floor
909 sq. ft.

MBr
14-10x13-6

Br 3
11-6x10-10

Dn

plant
shelf

open to
below

Br 2
11-8x17-0

52'-0"

© Copyright by
designer/architect

Brk
11-0x11-0

Dining
11-4x11-6

Kit
15-0x
11-4

Family
14-6x13-4

plant shelf

46'-0"

Living
13-4x15-6

vaulted

Up

Dn

Foyer

Garage
21-8x19-4

Porch

First Floor
1,136 sq. ft.

LOWE'S
LEGACY
SERIES

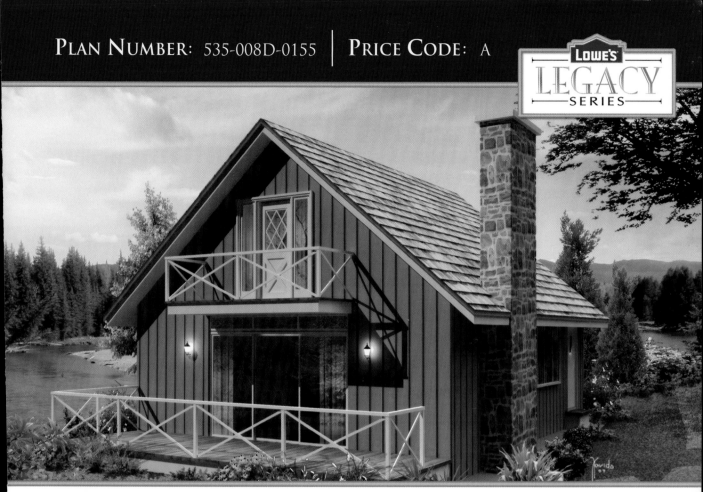

SPECIAL FEATURES

1,200 total square feet of living area

Ornate ranch-style railing enhances exterior while the stone fireplace provides a visual anchor

Spectacular living room features an inviting fireplace and adjoins a charming kitchen with dining area

Two second floor bedrooms share a half bath

3 bedrooms, 1 1/2 baths

Crawl space foundation, drawings also include slab foundation

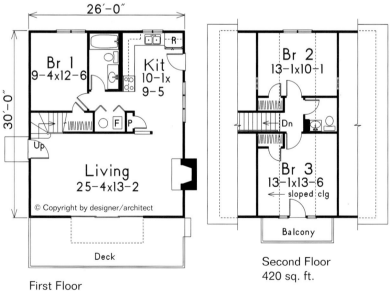

26'-0"

30'-0"

Br 1
9-4x12-6

Kit
10-1x
9-5

R

Up

F P

Living
25-4x13-2

© Copyright by designer/architect

Deck

First Floor
780 sq. ft.

Br 2
13-1x10-1

Dn

Br 3
13-1x13-6
← sloped clg

Balcony

Second Floor
420 sq. ft.

SPECIAL FEATURES

1,536 total square feet of living area

An amazing deck opens into a vaulted living room graced with an abundance of windows and a fireplace

The kitchen opens to the living area with a casual breakfast bar that is perfect for quick meals or buffet dinners

With one bedroom on the first floor and two on the second, there is plenty of room for family and friends

3 bedrooms, 2 baths

Basement foundation

Second Floor
576 sq. ft.

First Floor
960 sq. ft.

© Copyright by designer/architect

LOWE'S
LEGACY
SERIES

SPECIAL FEATURES

1,661 total square feet of living area

Large open foyer with angled wall arrangement and high ceiling adds to spacious living room

The kitchen and dining area have impressive cathedral ceilings and a French door allowing access to the rear patio

Utility room is conveniently located near the kitchen

Secluded master bedroom has a large walk-in closet, unique brick wall arrangement and 10' ceiling

3 bedrooms, 2 baths, 2-car garage

Slab foundation

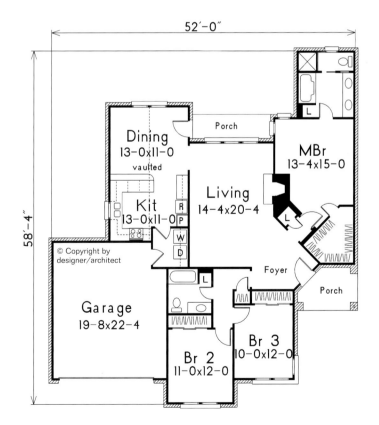

52'-0"

58'-4"

Dining
13-0x11-0
vaulted

Porch

MBr
13-4x15-0

Kit
13-0x11-0

Living
14-4x20-4

© Copyright by
designer/architect

Foyer

Porch

Garage
19-8x22-4

Br 2
11-0x12-0

Br 3
10-0x12-0

SPECIAL FEATURES

1,999 total square feet of living area

Center island in kitchen creates extra storage space and preparation area

All bedrooms on the second floor for privacy

Double-doors separate the formal living room from a more casual family room

3 bedrooms, 2 1/2 baths, 2-car side entry garage

Basement foundation, drawings also include crawl space foundation

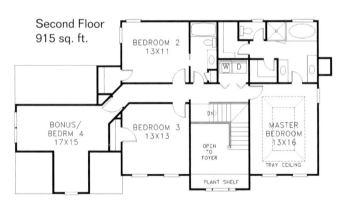

Second Floor
915 sq. ft.

BEDROOM 2
13X11

W D

BONUS/
BEDRM 4
17X15

BEDROOM 3
13X13

DN

OPEN
TO
FOYER

MASTER
BEDROOM
13X16

TRAY CEILING

PLANT SHELF

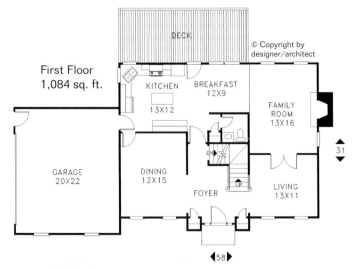

DECK

© Copyright by
designer/architect

First Floor
1,084 sq. ft.

KITCHEN
13X12

BREAKFAST
12X9

FAMILY
ROOM
13X16

GARAGE
20X22

DINING
12X15

DN

FOYER

UP

LIVING
13X11

31

◀58▶

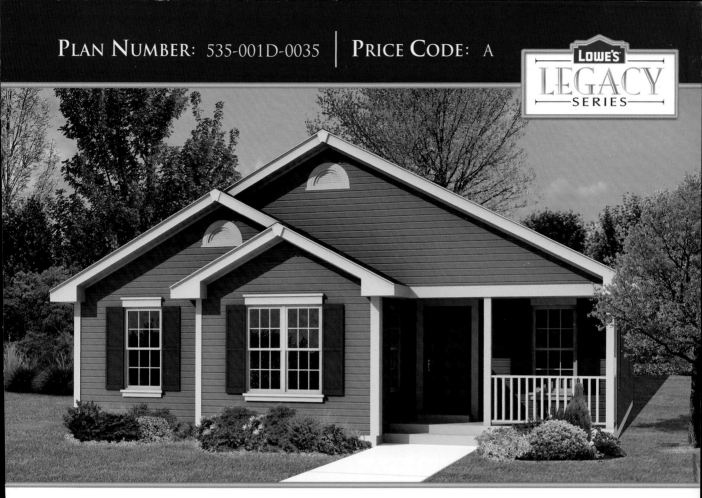

SPECIAL FEATURES

1,396 total square feet of living area

Gabled front adds interest to the facade

Living and dining rooms share a vaulted ceiling

Master bedroom features a walk-in closet and private bath

Functional kitchen boasts a center work island and convenient pantry

3 bedrooms, 2 baths, 1-car rear entry carport

Basement foundation, drawings also include crawl space foundation

© Copyright by designer/architect

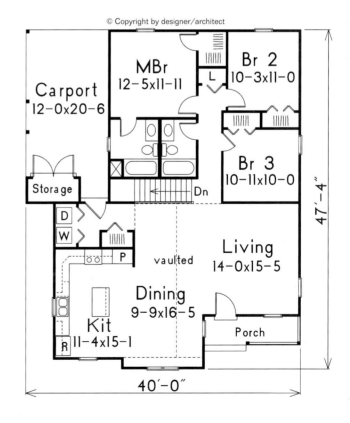

SPECIAL FEATURES

1,211 total square feet of living area

Extraordinary views are enjoyed in the vaulted family room through sliding doors

Functional kitchen features snack bar and laundry closet

Bedroom and bunk room complete first floor while a large bedroom with two storage areas and balcony complete the second floor

Additional plan for second floor creates 223 square feet of additional bedroom space

2 bedrooms, 1 bath

Crawl space foundation, drawings also include basement foundation

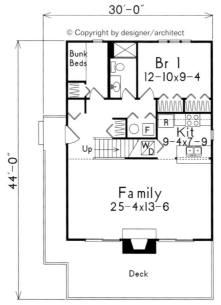

30'-0"

© Copyright by designer/architect

Bunk Beds

Br 1
12-10x9-4

Kit
9-4x7-9

Up

Family
25-4x13-6

44'-0"

Deck

First Floor
884 sq. ft.

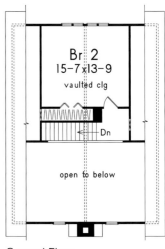

Br 2
15-7x13-9
vaulted clg

Dn

open to below

Second Floor
327 sq. ft.

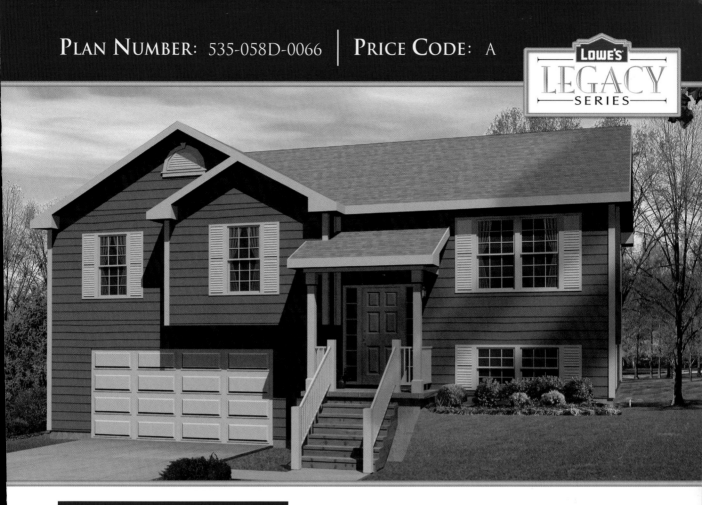

SPECIAL FEATURES

1,217 total square feet of living area

Step up into the main level to see an elegant family room with vaulted ceiling and grand fireplace flanked by windows

The kitchen/breakfast area enjoys a bright bay window with access to the outdoors

The master bedroom enjoys a walk-in closet, whirlpool tub and a double vanity

3 bedrooms, 2 baths, 2-car garage

Basement foundation

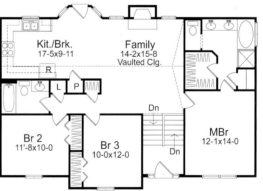

First Floor
1,217 sq. ft.

Kit./Brk.
17-5x9-11

Family
14-2x15-8
Vaulted Clg.

Br 2
11'-8x10-0

Br 3
10-0x12-0

MBr
12-1x14-0

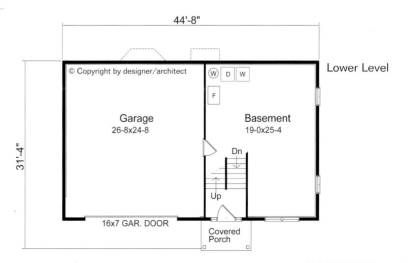

Lower Level

44'-8"

31'-4"

© Copyright by designer/architect

Garage
26-8x24-8

Basement
19-0x25-4

16x7 GAR. DOOR

Covered Porch

Lowe's LEGACY SERIES

SPECIAL FEATURES

1,496 total square feet of living area

Vaulted living and dining rooms create a
spacious feel to the main living areas

Breakfast area and kitchen
combine for convenience

Large master bath has all the amenities

Dining area has access onto the deck

3 bedrooms, 2 baths,
2-car drive under garage

Basement foundation

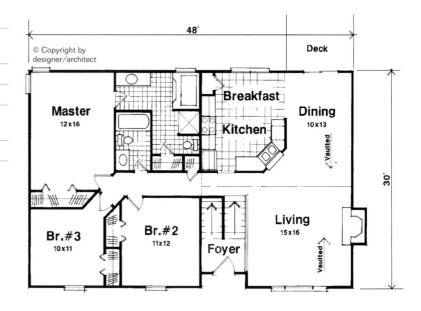

48'

© Copyright by
designer/architect

Deck

Master
12 x 16

Breakfast

Kitchen

Dining
10 x 13

Vaulted

30'

Br. #3
10 x 11

Br. #2
11 x 12

Foyer

Living
15 x 16

Vaulted

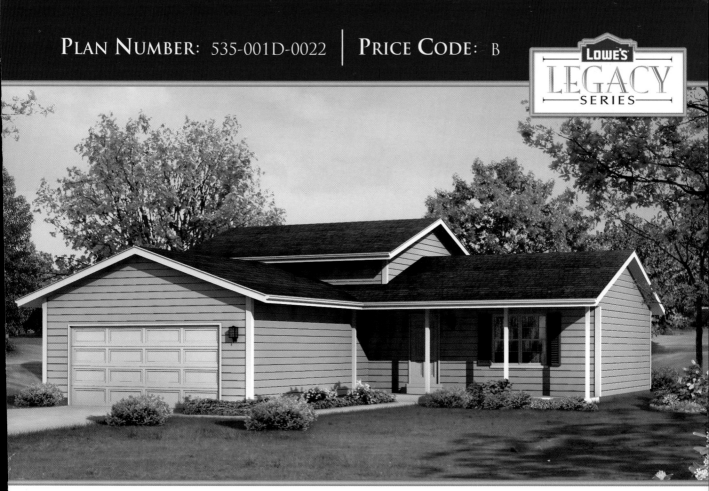

SPECIAL FEATURES

1,680 total square feet of living area

Country facade and covered front porch

Large basement area for family room, study or hobby area

Plenty of closet space throughout this design

3 bedrooms, 2 baths, 2-car garage

Partial basement/crawl space foundation

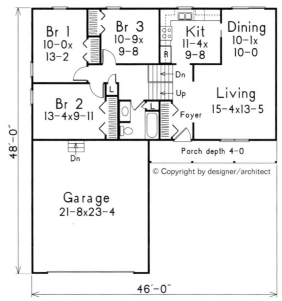

First Floor
1,104 sq. ft.

© Copyright by designer/architect

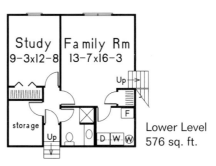

Lower Level
576 sq. ft.

SPECIAL FEATURES

1,969 total square feet of living area

An octagonal tower, covered porch, arched trim and boxed window decorate the exterior

The great room with fireplace, high windows and rear yard access provides an excellent atmosphere for family activities

Dramatic views to the great room and foyer are provided at the second floor balcony where there is ample room for a computer area or reading loft

The second floor bonus room has an additional 268 square feet of living space

3 bedrooms, 2 1/2 baths, 2-car garage

Basement foundation

Second Floor
549 sq. ft.

First Floor
1,420 sq. ft.

Width: 58'-0"
Depth: 44'-4"

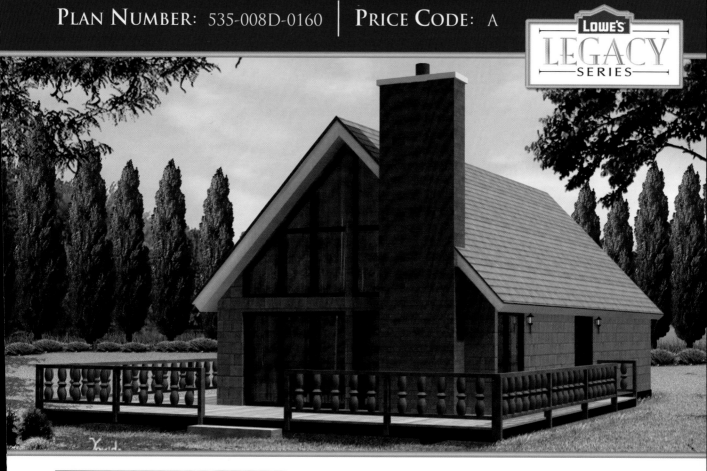

SPECIAL FEATURES

1,354 total square feet of living area

Soaring ceilings highlight the kitchen, living and dining areas creating dramatic excitement

A spectacular large deck surrounds the front and both sides of the home

An impressive U-shaped kitchen has a wrap-around breakfast bar and shares fantastic views with both the first and second floors through an awesome wall of glass

Two bedrooms with a bath, a sleeping loft and second floor balcony overlooking the living area complete the home

2 bedrooms, 1 bath

Crawl space foundation

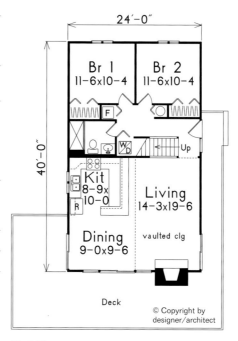

24'-0"

40'-0"

Br 1
11-6x10-4

Br 2
11-6x10-4

F

W D

Up

Kit
8-9x
10-0

R

Living
14-3x19-6

vaulted clg

Dining
9-0x9-6

Deck

© Copyright by designer/architect

First Floor
960 sq. ft.

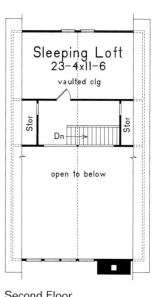

Sleeping Loft
23-4x11-6
vaulted clg

Stor

Dn

Stor

open to below

Second Floor
394 sq. ft.

SPECIAL FEATURES

1,631 total square feet of living area

9' ceilings throughout this home

Utility room is conveniently
located near the kitchen

Roomy kitchen and dining area boast
a breakfast bar and deck access

A raised ceiling accents the master bedroom

3 bedrooms, 2 baths,
2-car drive under garage

Basement foundation

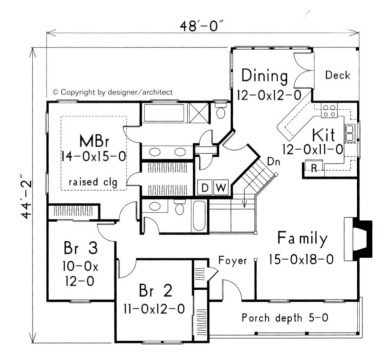

© Copyright by designer/architect

48'-0"

44'-2"

Dining 12-0x12-0

Deck

Kit 12-0x11-0

MBr 14-0x15-0
raised clg

D W

Dn

R

Br 3 10-0x 12-0

Br 2 11-0x12-0

Family 15-0x18-0

Foyer

Porch depth 5-0

SPECIAL FEATURES

701 total square feet of living area

Covered stairs lead into the living area

The open floor plan adds spaciousness

The utility room has space for a
washer and dryer and storage

1 bedroom, 1 bath, 2-car garage

Basement foundation

Second Floor
701 sq. ft.

30'-0"

28'-0"

Kitchen
8-4x7

Dining
13x10-4

MBr.
12x10-9

Great Room
13x11

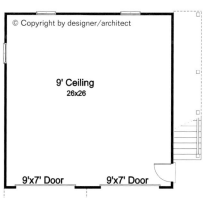

First Floor

© Copyright by designer/architect

9' Ceiling
26x26

9'x7' Door   9'x7' Door

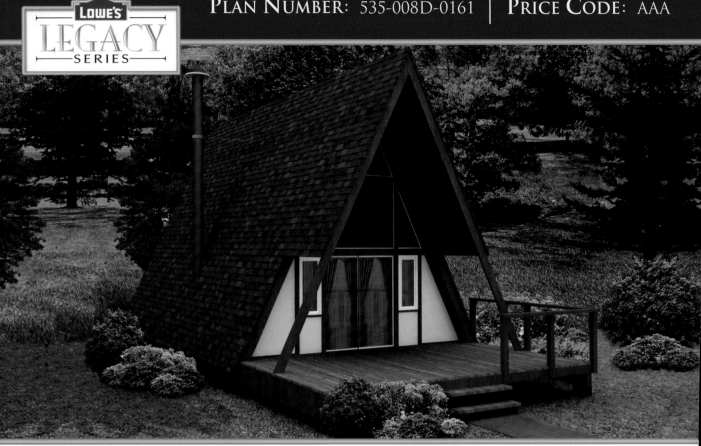

SPECIAL FEATURES

618 total square feet of living area

Memorable family events are certain to be enjoyed on this fabulous partially covered deck

Equally impressive is the living area with its cathedral ceiling and exposed rafters

A kitchenette, bedroom and bath conclude the first floor with a delightful sleeping loft on the second floor

1 bedroom, 1 bath

Pier foundation

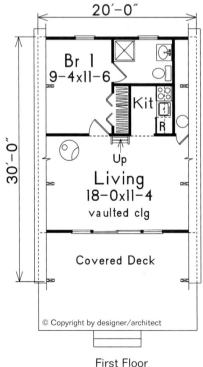

© Copyright by designer/architect

First Floor
480 sq. ft.

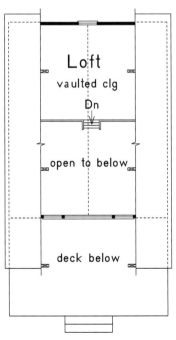

Second Floor
138 sq. ft.

SPECIAL FEATURES

1,832 total square feet of living area

9' ceilings throughout most of the home and a sloping 13' ceiling in the family room increase the spaciousness of this design

A U-shaped kitchen featuring a center island opens to the windowed dining area for an exceptional gathering space

The optional bonus room on the second floor has an additional 267 square feet of living area

3 bedrooms, 2 1/2 baths, 2-car garage

Crawl space foundation

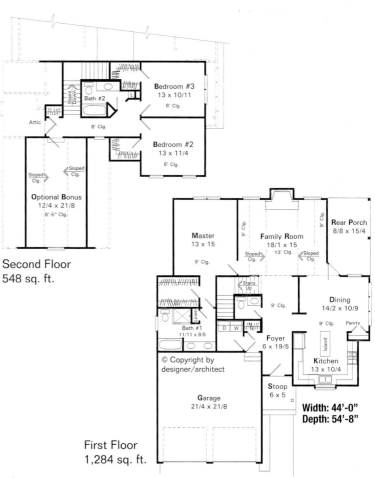

Second Floor
548 sq. ft.

First Floor
1,284 sq. ft.

Width: 44'-0"
Depth: 54'-8"

Lowe's
LEGACY
SERIES

SPECIAL FEATURES

2,095 total square feet of living area

Energy efficient home with
2" x 6" exterior walls

The foyer opens to the formal
living room defined by decorative
columns and the spacious living
room, both featuring 11' ceilings

A double-door entry leads to the
relaxing master bedroom with
walk-in closet and deluxe bath

A large utility room includes a coat
closet and is accessed through
the kitchen and garage

3 bedrooms, 2 baths, 3-car side entry garage

Basement foundation

© Copyright by designer/architect

LOWE'S
LEGACY
SERIES

SPECIAL FEATURES

448 total square feet of living area

Bedroom features a large
walk-in closet ideal for storage

Combined dining/sitting area
is ideal for relaxing

Galley-style kitchen is compact and efficient

Covered porch adds to front facade

1 bedroom, 1 bath

Slab foundation

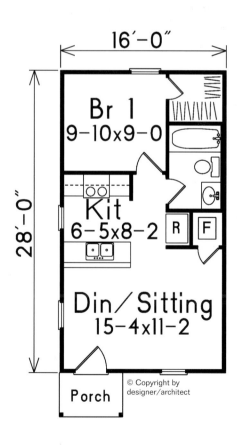

16'-0"

28'-0"

Br 1
9-10x9-0

Kit
6-5x8-2

R   F

Din/Sitting
15-4x11-2

© Copyright by
designer/architect

Porch

LOWE'S LEGACY SERIES

SPECIAL FEATURES

2,103 total square feet of living area

This country style bungalow offers casual living perfect for family

The large country kitchen invites large gatherings with plenty of space for dining

The loft/bedroom #4 can remain open or a wall can be added for more privacy

4 bedrooms, 2 1/2 baths, 2-car garage

Basement foundation

Second Floor
695 sq. ft.

Br 2
11-8x14-10

Loft/Br 4
12-6x10

Optional Wall

Br 3
11x13-6

DN

OPEN TO BELOW

DORMER OPEN BELOW

L

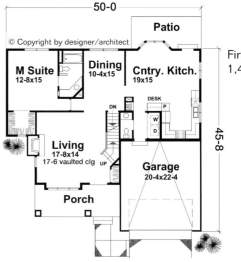

First Floor
1,408 sq. ft.

50-0

45-8

Patio

© Copyright by designer/architect

M Suite
12-8x15

Dining
10-4x15

Cntry. Kitch.
19x15

DESK

P

DN

W
D

Living
17-8x14
17-6 vaulted clg

UP

Garage
20-4x22-4

Porch

SPECIAL FEATURES

1,568 total square feet of living area

A classic hip roof with multiple gables, roof dormers and decorative circular windows are all combined to create this home's stylish facade

The great room includes a vaulted ceiling with plant shelf, fireplace and is open to a bayed breakfast room

A walk-in pantry is featured in the well-designed kitchen and is adjacent to a convenient laundry room

The master bedroom with double entry doors is nicely appointed with an oversized bath and large walk-in closet

3 bedrooms, 2 baths, 2-car garage

Crawl space foundation, drawings also include slab foundation

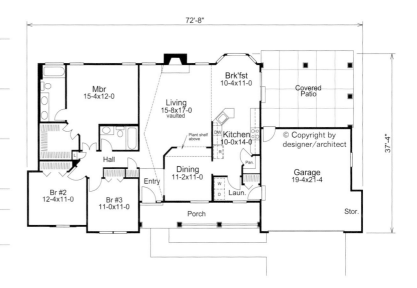

72'-8"

Mbr
15-4x12-0

Brk'fst
10-4x11-0

Covered
Patio

Living
15-8x17-0
vaulted

Plant shelf
above

Kitchen
10-0x14-0

© Copyright by
designer/architect

Hall

Dining
11-2x11-0

Pan.

Garage
19-4x21-4

37'-4"

Br #2
12-4x11-0

Br #3
11-0x11-0

Entry

Laun.

Porch

Stor.

LEGACY
SERIES

SPECIAL FEATURES

1,536 total square feet of living area

Formal living room featured in
the front of the home

Combined living areas create the
back of the home with great room,
dining area and kitchen all in one

Second floor master bedroom
includes a private bath

3 bedrooms, 2 1/2 baths, 1-car garage

Basement foundation, drawings also
include crawl space and slab foundations

One Car 37'-8"
Two Car 45'-8"

Dining
10-8x7-6

Great Rm
12-8x12-11

© Copyright by
designer/architect

Kit
10-8x8-0

36'-0"

Living Rm
11-7x15-1

Garage
13-4x21-4

Two
Car

Dn

Up

Foyer

Porch

First Floor
768 sq. ft.

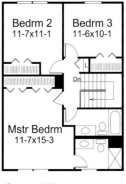

Bedrm 2
11-7x11-1

Bedrm 3
11-6x10-1

Dn

Mstr Bedrm
11-7x15-3

Second Floor
768 sq. ft.

SPECIAL FEATURES

2,164 total square feet of living area

Energy efficient home with
2" x 6" exterior walls

Great design for entertaining with a wet bar
and see-through fireplace in the great room

Plenty of closet space

Vaulted ceilings enlarge the master bedroom,
great room and kitchen/breakfast area

Great room features great view
to the rear of the home

3 bedrooms, 2 1/2 baths,
2-car side entry garage

Basement foundation

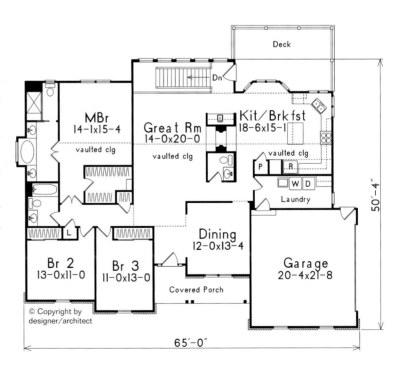

LOWE'S LEGACY SERIES

SPECIAL FEATURES

1,776 total square feet of living area

Master bedroom has a double-door entry into the formal living room

Large foyer has plenty of room for greeting guests

Great room is open to the second floor and features a fireplace flanked by windows

3 bedrooms, 2 1/2 baths, 2-car side entry garage

Walk-out basement foundation

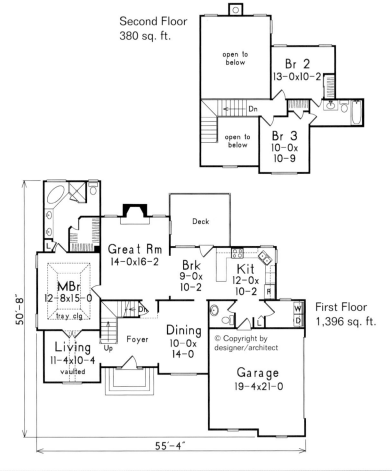

Second Floor 380 sq. ft.

open to below

Br 2 13-0x10-2

Dn

open to below

Br 3 10-0x 10-9

First Floor 1,396 sq. ft.

Deck

Great Rm 14-0x16-2

Brk 9-0x 10-2

Kit 12-0x 10-2

MBr 12-8x15-0 tray clg

Foyer

Up

Dining 10-0x 14-0

© Copyright by designer/architect

Living 11-4x10-4 vaulted

Garage 19-4x21-0

50'-8"

55'-4"

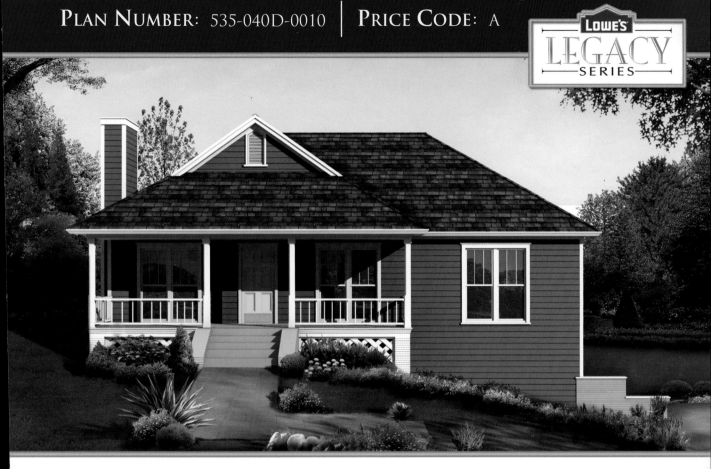

SPECIAL FEATURES

1,496 total square feet of living area

Master bedroom features a tray ceiling, walk-in closet and spacious bath

Vaulted ceiling and fireplace grace the family room

Dining room is adjacent to the kitchen and features access to the rear porch

Convenient access to the utility room from the kitchen

3 bedrooms, 2 baths, 2-car drive under garage

Basement foundation

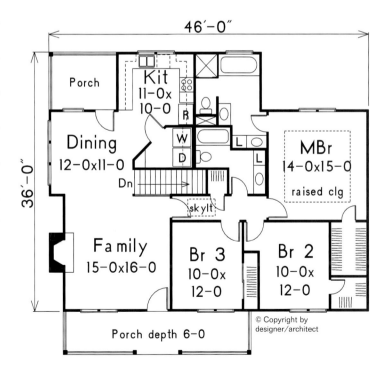

46'-0"

36'-0"

Porch

Kit
11-0x 10-0

Dining
12-0x11-0

Dn

skylt

MBr
14-0x15-0

raised clg

Family
15-0x16-0

Br 3
10-0x 12-0

Br 2
10-0x 12-0

© Copyright by designer/architect

Porch depth 6-0

SPECIAL FEATURES

1,806 total square feet of living area

Wrap-around deck, great for entertaining, enhances appearance

Side entry foyer accesses two rear bedrooms, hall bath and living and dining area

L-shaped kitchen is open to dining areas

Lots of living area is provided on the lower level, including a spacious family room with a fireplace and sliding doors to the patio under the deck

3 bedrooms, 2 baths

Walk-out basement foundation

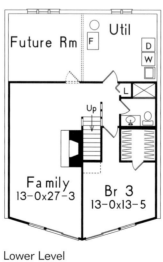

Lower Level
742 sq. ft.

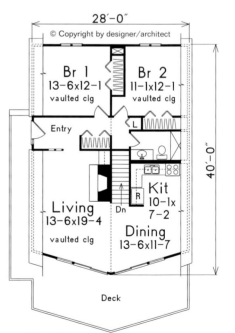

First Floor
1,064 sq. ft.

SPECIAL FEATURES

1,895 total square feet of living area

Energy efficient home with
2" x 6" exterior walls

The foyer opens into the airy great
room that features a grand fireplace

The kitchen/breakfast area enjoys
a work island, built-in desk, walk-in
pantry and access to the outdoors

Both baths include a double
vanity for convenience

3 bedrooms, 2 baths, 2-car garage

Basement foundation

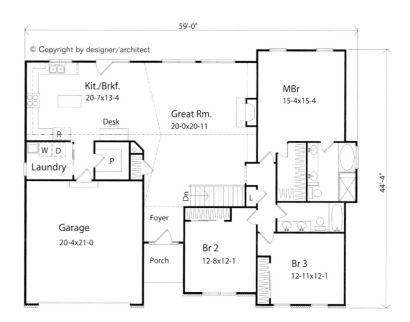

© Copyright by designer/architect

59'-0"

44'-4"

Kit./Brkf.
20-7x13-4

Desk

R

W D

Laundry

P

MBr
15-4x15-4

Great Rm.
20-0x20-11

Dn

L

Garage
20-4x21-0

Foyer

Porch

Br 2
12-8x12-1

Br 3
12-11x12-1

LOWE'S LEGACY SERIES

SPECIAL FEATURES

1,770 total square feet of living area

Distinctive covered entrance
leads into spacious foyer

Master bedroom, living and dining rooms
feature large windows for plenty of light

Oversized living room has a high ceiling
and large windows that flank the fireplace

Kitchen includes a pantry and
large planning center

Master bedroom has a high vaulted ceiling,
deluxe bath, and private access outdoors

3 bedrooms, 2 baths, 2-car garage

Slab foundation

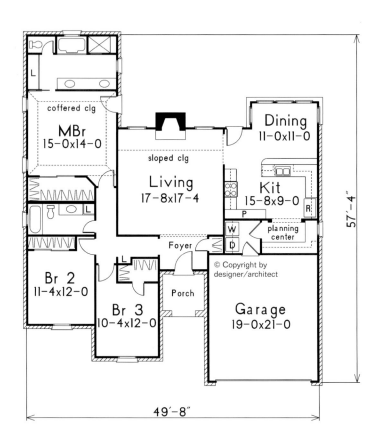

coffered clg

MBr
15-0x14-0

sloped clg

Living
17-8x17-4

Dining
11-0x11-0

Kit
15-8x9-0

P

planning center

W
D

Foyer

Br 2
11-4x12-0

© Copyright by
designer/architect

Br 3
10-4x12-0

Porch

Garage
19-0x21-0

57'-4"

49'-8"

LOWE'S LEGACY SERIES

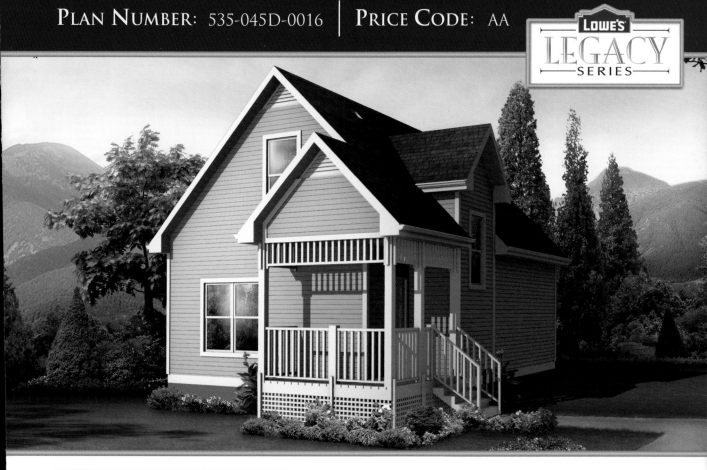

SPECIAL FEATURES

1,107 total square feet of living area

L-shaped kitchen has a serving bar overlooking the dining/living room

Second floor bedrooms share a bath with the linen closet

Front porch opens into the foyer with convenient coat closet

3 bedrooms, 2 baths

Basement foundation

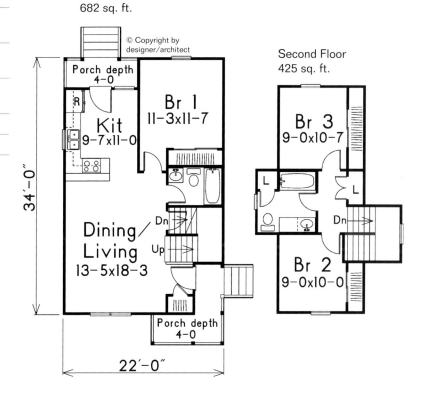

First Floor
682 sq. ft.

© Copyright by designer/architect

Porch depth 4-0

Kit 9-7x11-0

Br 1 11-3x11-7

Dining/Living 13-5x18-3

Dn

Up

34'-0"

Porch depth 4-0

22'-0"

Second Floor
425 sq. ft.

Br 3 9-0x10-7

L

L

Dn

Br 2 9-0x10-0

SPECIAL FEATURES

2,050 total square feet of living area

Energy efficient home with
2" x 6" exterior walls

Large kitchen and dining area has
access to the garage and porch

Master bedroom features unique turret
design, private bath and large walk-in closet

3 bedrooms, 2 1/2 baths,
2-car side entry garage

Basement foundation, drawings also
include crawl space and slab foundations

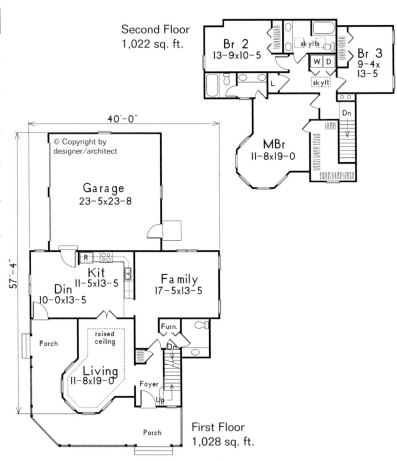

Second Floor
1,022 sq. ft.

Br 2
13-9x10-5

skylts

Br 3
9-4x
13-5

W D

skylt

Dn

MBr
11-8x19-0

40'-0"

© Copyright by
designer/architect

Garage
23-5x23-8

57'-4"

R

Kit
11-5x13-5

Din
10-0x13-5

Family
17-5x13-5

Furn.

raised
ceiling

Dn

Porch

Living
11-8x19-0

Foyer

Up

First Floor
1,028 sq. ft.

Porch

SPECIAL FEATURES

1,317 total square feet of living area

Galley-style kitchen includes substantial cabinets and counterspace

Dining area is joined by the great room creating an open atmosphere

The lovely patio off the dining area brings the outdoors in

A well-designed laundry area is nestled between the garage and kitchen

3 bedrooms, 2 baths, 2-car garage

Basement foundation, drawings also include crawl space and slab foundations

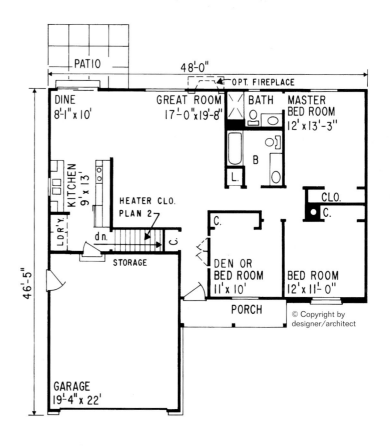

PATIO

48'-0"

OPT. FIREPLACE

DINE 8'-1" x 10'

GREAT ROOM 17'-0" x19'-8"

BATH

MASTER BED ROOM 12' x 13'-3"

B

L.

KITCHEN 9' x 13'

HEATER CLO. PLAN 2

CLO.

C.

LDR'Y.

d n.

C.

C.

DEN OR BED ROOM 11' x 10'

BED ROOM 12' x 11'-0"

STORAGE

PORCH

46'-5"

© Copyright by designer/architect

GARAGE 19'-4" x 22'

LOWE'S
LEGACY
SERIES

SPECIAL FEATURES

2,128 total square feet of living area

Large bonus area over the garage, which is included in the square footage, converts to a fourth bedroom or activity center

Family room fireplace and vaulted ceiling provide an attractive entry

Master bedroom features a bath with windowed tub, walk-in closet, separate shower and plenty of storage space

3 bedrooms, 2 1/2 baths, 2-car side entry garage

Basement foundation

Second Floor
905 sq. ft.

First Floor
1,223 sq. ft.

SPECIAL FEATURES

1,703 total square feet of living area

A large fireplace, plant shelf and access onto the patio enhance the spacious living room

Protected front entry includes a raised ceiling in the foyer

Master bedroom enjoys a walk-in closet, vaulted ceiling and window seats

Plan is well-suited for a narrow lot

3 bedrooms, 2 1/2 baths, 2-car garage

Slab foundation, drawings also include crawl space foundation

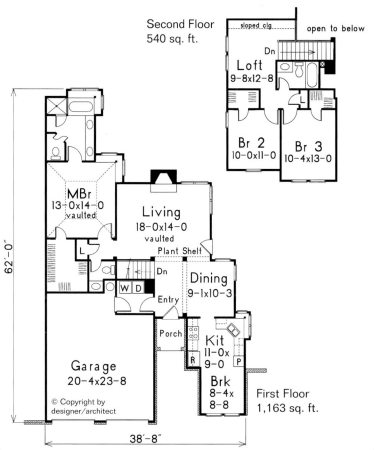

Second Floor
540 sq. ft.

sloped clg.   open to below

Dn

Loft
9-8x12-8

Br 2
10-0x11-0

Br 3
10-4x13-0

MBr
13-0x14-0
vaulted

Living
18-0x14-0
vaulted

Plant Shelf

Dining
9-1x10-3

Dn

W D

Entry

Porch

Kit
11-0x
9-0

R

P

Garage
20-4x23-8

Brk
8-4x
8-8

First Floor
1,163 sq. ft.

62'-0"

38'-8"

© Copyright by
designer/architect

SPECIAL FEATURES

1,971 total square feet of living area

Great room, kitchen and breakfast area unite to provide a central living space

Unique parlor offers place for conversation off the dining area

Deluxe master bedroom has a walk-in closet and sunny master bath

3 bedrooms, 2 1/2 baths, optional 2-car garage

Basement foundation

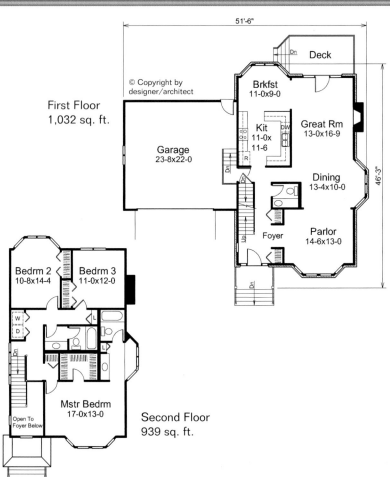

51'-6"

Deck

© Copyright by designer/architect

First Floor
1,032 sq. ft.

Brkfst
11-0x9-0

Garage
23-8x22-0

Kit
11-0x
11-6

Great Rm
13-0x16-9

Dining
13-4x10-0

Foyer

Parlor
14-6x13-0

46'-3"

Bedrm 2
10-8x14-4

Bedrm 3
11-0x12-0

W
D

Mstr Bedrm
17-0x13-0

Open To
Foyer Below

Second Floor
939 sq. ft.

SPECIAL FEATURES

1,020 total square feet of living area

Living room is warmed by a fireplace

Dining and living rooms are enhanced by vaulted ceilings and plant shelves

U-shaped kitchen features a large window over the sink

2 bedrooms, 1 bath

Slab foundation

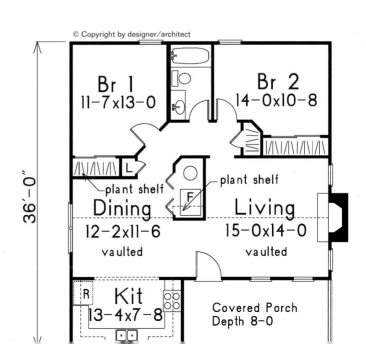

© Copyright by designer/architect

Br 1
11-7x13-0

Br 2
14-0x10-8

plant shelf

L

plant shelf

F

Dining
12-2x11-6
vaulted

Living
15-0x14-0
vaulted

36'-0"

R

Kit
13-4x7-8

Covered Porch
Depth 8-0

SPECIAL FEATURES

1,203 total square feet of living area

Large porch for quiet evening relaxation

The living room features a vaulted ceiling, fireplace and dining area with patio views

The kitchen includes an abundance of cabinet storage, a large walk-in pantry and door to the rear yard

The master bedroom has a vaulted ceiling, private bath with built-in linen storage and a walk-in closet

4 bedrooms, 2 1/2 baths, 2-car garage

Basement foundation, drawings also include slab and crawl space foundations

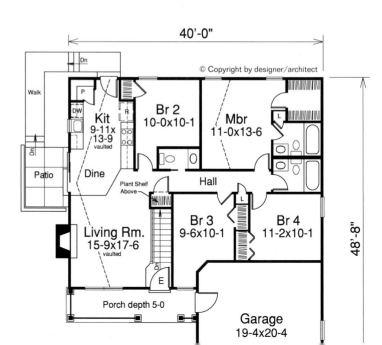

40'-0"

© Copyright by designer/architect

Walk

Dn

P

DW

Dn

Kit
9-11x
13-9
vaulted

Dine

Patio

Br 2
10-0x10-1

Mbr
11-0x13-6

L

Plant Shelf
Above

Hall

Living Rm.
15-9x17-6
vaulted

Br 3
9-6x10-1

L

Br 4
11-2x10-1

48'-8"

Porch depth 5-0

Garage
19-4x20-4

LOWE'S
LEGACY
SERIES

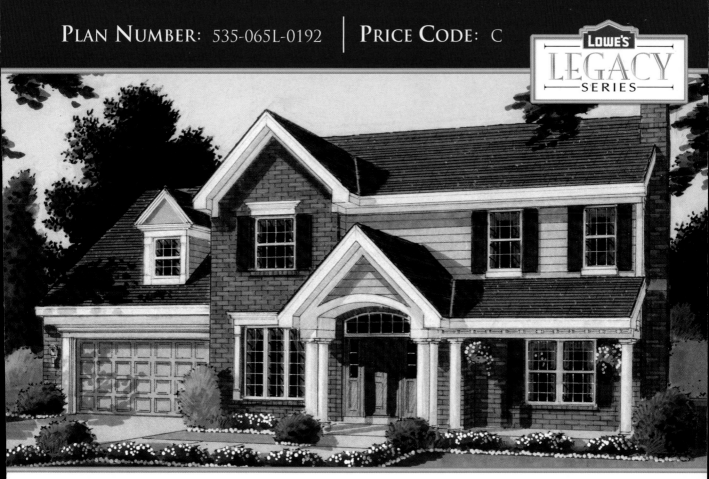

SPECIAL FEATURES

1,987 total square feet of living area

The wood rail at the stairs and the sunken great room create a charming first impression

A solarium with rear yard access offers a cozy and bright sitting area

The second floor houses three bedrooms, including the spacious master suite with 9' raised ceiling and deluxe bath to pamper the homeowner

The second floor bonus room has an additional 267 square feet of living space

3 bedrooms, 2 1/2 baths, 2-car garage

Basement foundation

Second Floor 927 sq. ft.

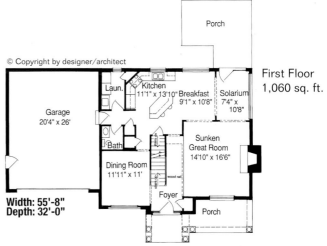

First Floor 1,060 sq. ft.

© Copyright by designer/architect

Width: 55'-8"
Depth: 32'-0"

LOWE'S LEGACY SERIES

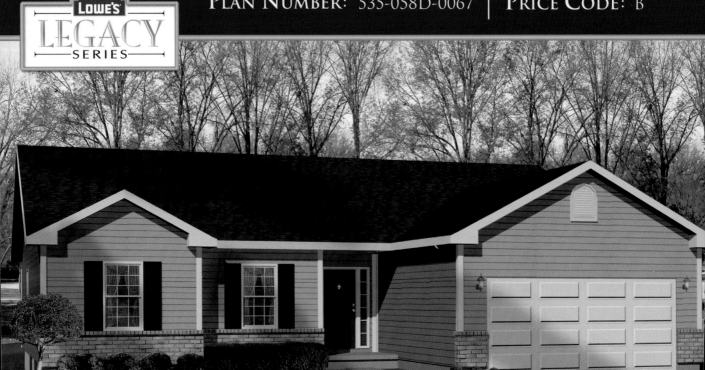

SPECIAL FEATURES

1,587 total square feet of living area

The spacious family room features a vaulted ceiling, fireplace and convenient coat closet

The kitchen/breakfast area is brightened by a large window and includes a convenient pantry

Secondary bedrooms are generously sized and share a full bath

3 bedrooms, 2 baths, 2-car garage

Basement foundation

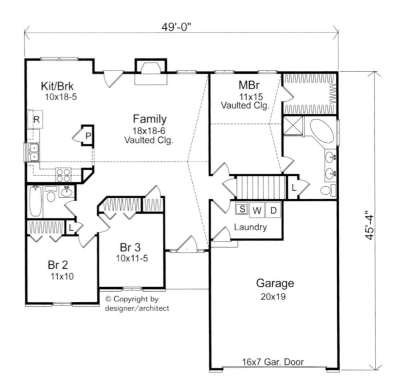

49'-0"

Kit/Brk
10x18-5

R

P

Family
18x18-6
Vaulted Clg.

MBr
11x15
Vaulted Clg.

L

S W D

Laundry

Br 2
11x10

Br 3
10x11-5

Garage
20x19

45'-4"

© Copyright by designer/architect

16x7 Gar. Door

SPECIAL FEATURES

1,436 total square feet of living area

Energy efficient home with
2" x 6" exterior walls

Corner fireplace warms the
living and dining rooms

The kitchen and nook combine for
a spacious informal living area

Bedrooms are located away from
main living areas for privacy

3 bedrooms, 2 baths, 2-car garage

Basement foundation

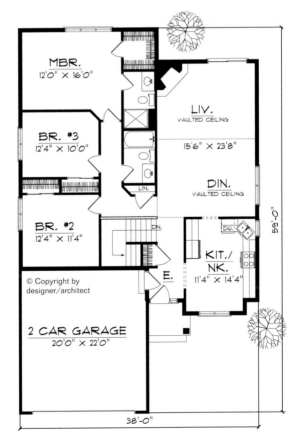

MBR.
12'0" X 16'0"

LIV.
VAULTED CEILING
15'6" X 23'8"

BR. #3
12'4" X 10'0"

DIN.
VAULTED CEILING

LIN.

BR. #2
12'4" X 11'4"

DN.

KIT./
NK.
11'4" X 14'4"

E.

© Copyright by
designer/architect

2 CAR GARAGE
20'0" X 22'0"

59'-0"

38'-0"

SPECIAL FEATURES

1,980 total square feet of living area

Curb appeal is captured with multi-level roof, gables and palladian windows

Step down into a magnificent, windowed living room and activity area adorned with a cozy fireplace, wet bar, and pass-through to the kitchen

The kitchen features plenty of storage space and an eat-in area

A delightful sitting room accesses the second floor bedrooms and offers a view to the step-up foyer below

3 bedrooms, 2 1/2 baths, 2-car garage

Basement foundation

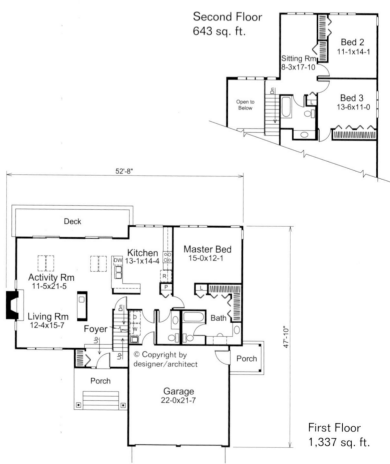

Second Floor
643 sq. ft.

Bed 2
11-1x14-1

Sitting Rm
8-3x17-10

Bed 3
13-6x11-0

Open to
Below

52'-8"

Deck

Kitchen
13-1x14-4

Master Bed
15-0x12-1

Activity Rm
11-5x21-5

Living Rm
12-4x15-7

Bath

Foyer

© Copyright by
designer/architect

Porch

47'-10"

Porch

Garage
22-0x21-7

First Floor
1,337 sq. ft.

SPECIAL FEATURES

1,976 total square feet of living area

Compact ranch features garage
entry near front door

Vaulted living area has large balcony above

Isolated master bedroom enjoys a
coffered ceiling and luxurious bath

Loft area has access to plenty of attic
storage and the future play room which has
an additional 174 square feet of living area

3 bedrooms, 2 baths, 2-car side entry garage

Basement foundation

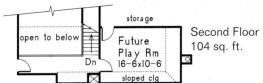

storage

open to below

Future
Play Rm
16-6x10-6

Dn

sloped clg

Second Floor
104 sq. ft.

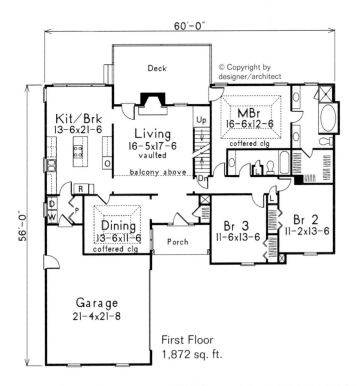

60'-0"

Deck

© Copyright by
designer/architect

Kit/Brk
13-6x21-6

Living
16-5x17-6
vaulted

Up

MBr
16-6x12-6

coffered clg

balcony above

Dn

56'-0"

R

D
W
P

Dining
13-6x11-6
coffered clg

Porch

Br 3
11-6x13-6

Br 2
11-2x13-6

Garage
21-4x21-8

First Floor
1,872 sq. ft.

SPECIAL FEATURES

953 total square feet of living area

Relax on porches fit for
charming rocking chairs

With two large bedrooms that feature
oversized closets, a spacious kitchen
and a family room with a fireplace,
this home has everything you need
to enjoy a vacation getaway

The kitchen has a sunny corner double sink,
roomy center island/snack bar and shares
a vaulted ceiling with the family room

2 bedrooms, 1 1/2 baths

Crawl space foundation

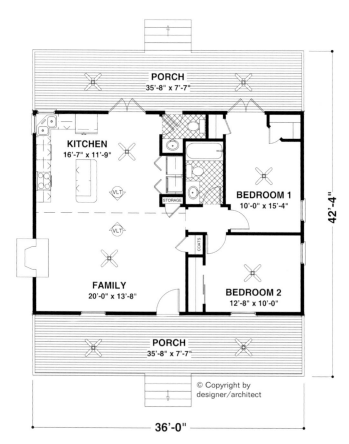

PORCH
35'-8" x 7'-7"

KITCHEN
16'-7" x 11'-9"

STORAGE

VLT

VLT

BEDROOM 1
10'-0" x 15'-4"

COATS

FAMILY
20'-0" x 13'-8"

BEDROOM 2
12'-8" x 10'-0"

PORCH
35'-8" x 7'-7"

42'-4"

36'-0"

LOWE'S
LEGACY
SERIES

SPECIAL FEATURES

1,897 total square feet of living area

The kitchen/breakfast room is spacious enough for plenty of family to relax and dine without feeling crowded

A corner whirlpool tub and large walk-in closet are great additions to the master bedroom

A large open loft area on the second floor offers casual gathering space perfect for a children's playroom

The bonus room above the garage has an additional 264 square feet of living area

2" x 6" exterior walls available, please order plan #535-058D-0125

3 bedrooms, 2 1/2 baths, 2-car garage

Basement foundation

Second Floor
626 sq. ft.

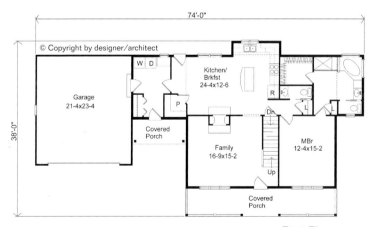

First Floor
1,271 sq. ft.

SPECIAL FEATURES

1,293 total square feet of living area

A very affordable ranch home that's easy to build

Living room has separate entry, guest closet and opens to the dining area

Eat-in L-shaped kitchen offers pass-through to family room

Master bedroom has its own bath and large walk-in closet

3 bedrooms, 2 baths, 1-car garage

Basement foundation, drawings also include crawl space foundation

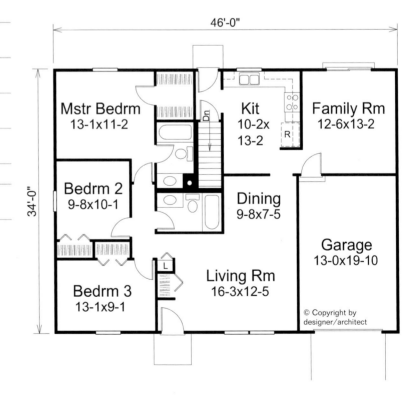

46'-0"

34'-0"

Mstr Bedrm
13-1x11-2

Kit
10-2x
13-2

Family Rm
12-6x13-2

Bedrm 2
9-8x10-1

Dining
9-8x7-5

Garage
13-0x19-10

Bedrm 3
13-1x9-1

Living Rm
16-3x12-5

© Copyright by designer/architect

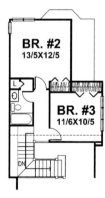

LOWE'S
LEGACY
SERIES

SPECIAL FEATURES

1,941 total square feet of living area

This home is designed to easily fit a narrow lot with its side entry

A corner window brightens the vaulted living room and adds style to the exterior

Bay windows accent the master bedroom and breakfast room, adding elegance and natural light

3 bedrooms, 2 1/2 baths, 2-car garage

Basement foundation

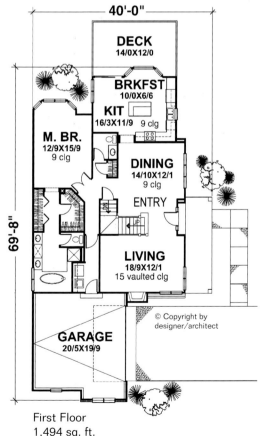

40'-0"

DECK
14/0X12/0

BRKFST
10/0X6/6

KIT
16/3X11/9
9 clg

M. BR.
12/9X15/9
9 clg

DINING
14/10X12/1
9 clg

ENTRY

69'-8"

LIVING
18/9X12/1
15 vaulted clg

© Copyright by designer/architect

GARAGE
20/5X19/9

First Floor
1,494 sq. ft.

BR. #2
13/5X12/5

BR. #3
11/6X10/5

DN

Second Floor
447 sq. ft.

SPECIAL FEATURES

1,850 total square feet of living area

Large living room with fireplace is illuminated by three second story skylights

Living and dining rooms are separated by a low wall while the dining room and kitchen are separated by a snack bar creating a spacious atmosphere

Master bedroom has a huge bath with double vanity and large walk-in closet

Two second floor bedrooms share a uniquely designed bath with skylight

3 bedrooms, 2 1/2 baths, 2-car garage

Basement foundation

Second Floor
630 sq. ft.

Bedrm 2
10-0x14-8

Bedrm 3
12-0x14-7

Open To Below

Dn

Open To Below

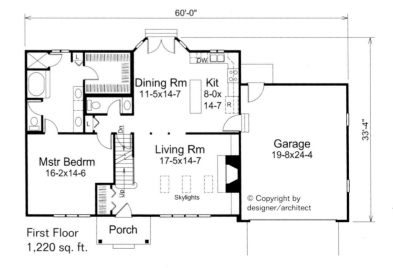

60'-0"

33'-4"

Dining Rm
11-5x14-7

Kit
8-0x
14-7

DW

R

Mstr Bedrm
16-2x14-6

Dn

Living Rm
17-5x14-7

Garage
19-8x24-4

Skylights

© Copyright by designer/architect

Up

First Floor
1,220 sq. ft.

Porch

SPECIAL FEATURES

1,416 total square feet of living area

Energy efficient home with
2" x 6" exterior walls

A breakfast nook extends off the
kitchen and has a vaulted ceiling
for a spacious, open feel

The large vaulted family room is the
perfect place to enjoy the warmth of
the fireplace or watch a movie

A large walk-in pantry organizes the
kitchen designed for efficiency

2 bedrooms, 2 baths, 1-car garage

Basement foundation

SPECIAL FEATURES

999 total square feet of living area

The dramatic entry is brightened by a glass front door and an arched transom window

Vaulted ceilings adorn the kitchen, family and dining rooms providing a feeling of spaciousness

A future studio on the lower level has an additional 300 square feet of living area and features a bath and a kitchenette making it ideal for a college student or in-law

2 bedrooms, 2 baths, 2-car garage

Basement foundation

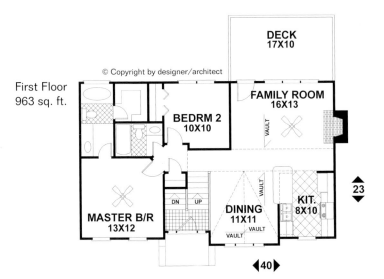

© Copyright by designer/architect

First Floor
963 sq. ft.

DECK
17X10

FAMILY ROOM
16X13

BEDRM 2
10X10

VAULT

MASTER B/R
13X12

DN   UP

DINING
11X11

KIT.
8X10

VAULT

VAULT

23

40

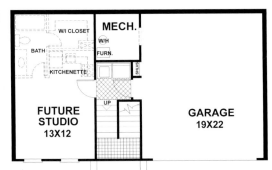

Lower Level
36 sq. ft.

W/I CLOSET

MECH.

BATH

W/H

FURN.

KITCHENETTE

SHLVS

UP

FUTURE
STUDIO
13X12

GARAGE
19X22

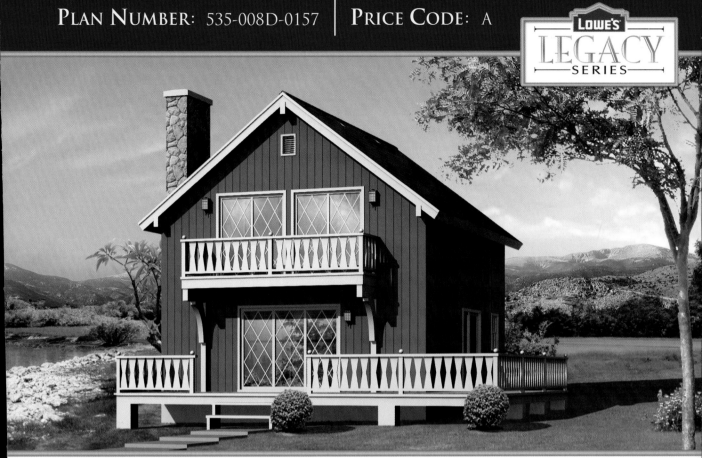

SPECIAL FEATURES

1,344 total square feet of living area

Beautiful stone fireplace, bracketed balcony and surrounding deck create an appealing atmosphere

Enormous living room, open to the dining area, enjoys views to the deck through two large sliding doors

Second floor delivers lots of sleeping area and views from the exterior balcony

5 bedrooms, 2 baths

Crawl space foundation

Second Floor
672 sq. ft.

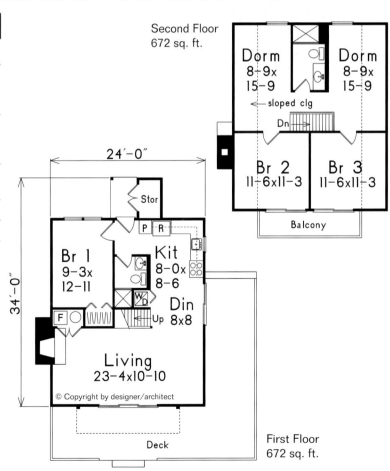

First Floor
672 sq. ft.

© Copyright by designer/architect

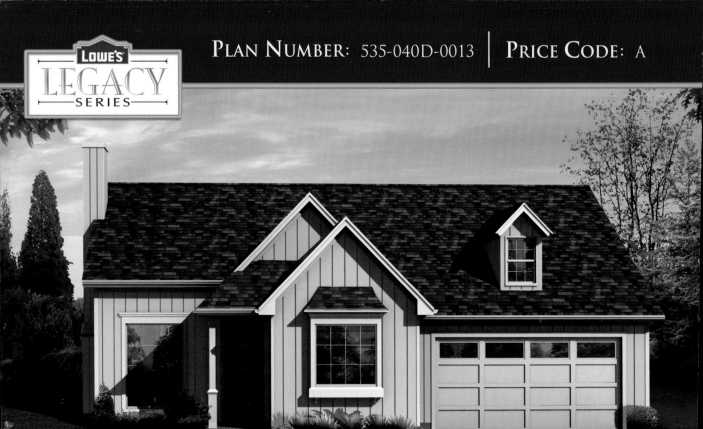

SPECIAL FEATURES

1,304 total square feet of living area

Covered entrance leads into the family room with a cozy fireplace

10' ceilings in kitchen, dining and family rooms

Master bedroom features a coffered ceiling, walk-in closet and private bath

Efficient kitchen includes large window over the sink

3 bedrooms, 2 baths, 2-car garage

Slab foundation

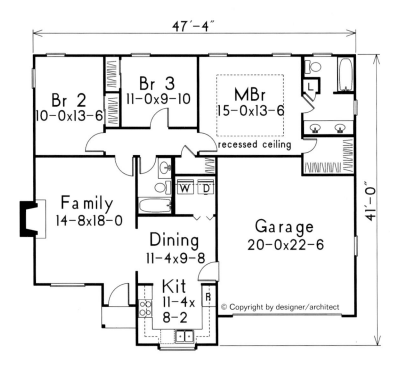

47'-4"

41'-0"

Br 2
10-0x13-6

Br 3
11-0x9-10

MBr
15-0x13-6

recessed ceiling

Family
14-8x18-0

W D

Dining
11-4x9-8

Garage
20-0x22-6

Kit
11-4x
8-2

R

© Copyright by designer/architect

SPECIAL FEATURES

751 total square feet of living area

Energy efficient home with
2" x 6" exterior walls

The covered porch expands the entire
width of this charming cottage

The kitchen/dining area and sitting nook
combine for increased spaciousness

Two bedrooms share a roomy bath

2 bedrooms, 1 bath

Crawl space foundation

32'-0"

36'-4"

Br 2
11-7x10-0

Sitting
12-1x7-0

Br 1
10-0x11-6

Kitchen/Dining
16-7x10-4

R

D

© Copyright by
designer/architect

Covered
Porch

Lowe's LEGACY SERIES

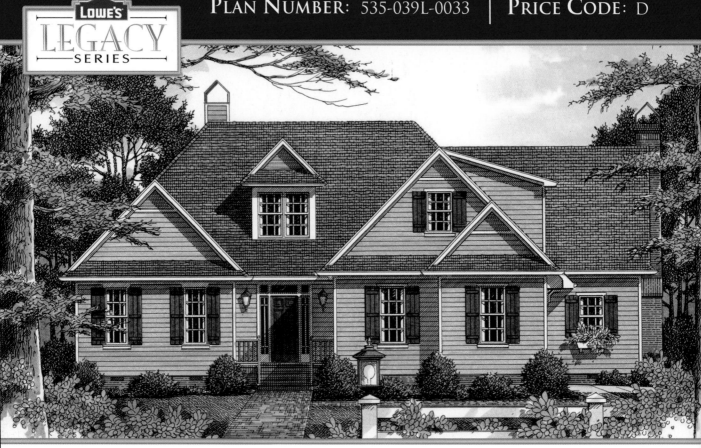

SPECIAL FEATURES

2,113 total square feet of living area

The dining room is situated between the organized kitchen and the cozy keeping room with fireplace for an open atmosphere

Bedroom #2 has access to the attic storage, a walk-in closet and a charming window seat

Optional bonus room on the second floor has an additional 331 square feet of living area

3 bedrooms, 2 1/2 baths,
2-car side entry garage

Crawl space foundation

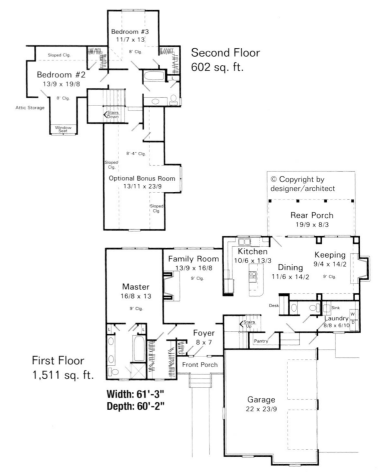

Bedroom #3
11/7 x 13

Sloped Clg.   8' Clg.

Bedroom #2
13/9 x 19/8

Second Floor
602 sq. ft.

Attic Storage

8' Clg.

Stairs Down

Window Seat

8'-4" Clg.

Sloped Clg.

Optional Bonus Room
13/11 x 23/9

Sloped Clg

© Copyright by designer/architect

Rear Porch
19/9 x 8/3

Family Room
13/9 x 16/8
9' Clg.

Kitchen
10/6 x 13/3

Dining
11/6 x 14/2

Keeping
9/4 x 14/2
9' Clg.

Master
16/8 x 13
9' Clg.

Desk

Sink

Laundry
8/8 x 6/10

Stairs Up

Foyer
8 x 7

Pantry

First Floor
1,511 sq. ft.

Front Porch

Width: 61'-3"
Depth: 60'-2"

Garage
22 x 23/9

SPECIAL FEATURES

1,872 total square feet of living area

Recessed porch has entry door with sidelights and roof dormers adding charm

Foyer with handcrafted stair adjoins living room with fireplace

First floor bedroom has access to bath and laundry room making it perfect for the master bedroom or a live-in parent

Largest of three second floor bedrooms enjoys double closets and private access to the hall bath

4 bedrooms, 2 baths, 2-car garage

Basement foundation, drawings also include crawl space and slab foundations

Bedrm 3
10-8x11-5

Mstr Bedrm
13-2x15-4

Bedrm 2
14-1x11-4

Second Floor
804 sq. ft.

58'-0"

© Copyright by designer/architect

Family Rm
16-1x12-1

Kitchen
11-1x12-1

dw R

Mud Rm

Garage
21-8x21-4

30'-8"

Living Rm
13-1x17-7

Bedrm/Dining
13-1x12-4

Foyer

First Floor
1,068 sq. ft.

SPECIAL FEATURES

2,128 total square feet of living area

Large bonus room offers many possibilities and is included in the second floor square footage

Convenient laundry room is located near the kitchen

Private master bath features a raised ceiling, large walk-in closet and deluxe bath

3 bedrooms, 2 1/2 baths, 2-car garage

Basement foundation

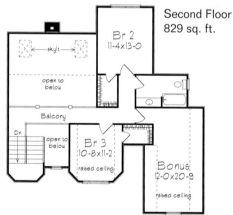

Second Floor
829 sq. ft.

Br 2
11-4x13-0

skylt

open to below

Balcony

Dn

open to below

Br 3
10-8x11-2
raised ceiling

Bonus
12-0x20-9
raised ceiling

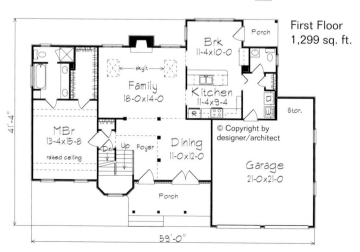

First Floor
1,299 sq. ft.

Brk
11-4x10-0

Porch

skylt

Family
18-0x14-0

Kitchen
11-4x9-4

Stor.

MBr
13-4x15-8
raised ceiling

Dn

Up   Foyer

Dining
11-0x12-0

© Copyright by designer/architect

Garage
21-0x21-0

41'-4"

Porch

59'-0"

LOWE'S LEGACY SERIES

SPECIAL FEATURES

1,536 total square feet of living area

9' ceilings throughout this home

All bedrooms are located on the second floor for privacy from living areas

Spacious great room has a corner fireplace and cheerful wall of windows

3 bedrooms, 2 1/2 baths, 2-car garage

Basement foundation

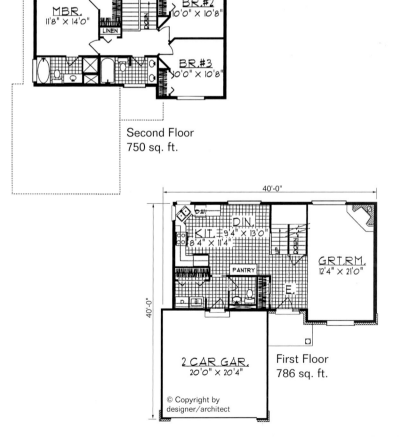

Second Floor
750 sq. ft.

First Floor
786 sq. ft.

© Copyright by
designer/architect

SPECIAL FEATURES

1,927 total square feet of living area

Stucco covered arches decorate a handsome covered entry porch

Large living room features a cozy fireplace and views into the dining area with a wide bay window

A smartly designed kitchen has all the amenities and opens to an expansive family room with fireplace

Second floor enjoys an exquisite master bedroom and has convenient laundry facilities

3 bedrooms, 2 1/2 baths, 2-car garage

Crawl space foundation

Second Floor
943 sq. ft.

Bed 2
10-3x11-8

Master Bed
17-9x14-10

Open to Below

Bed 3
11-8x12-6

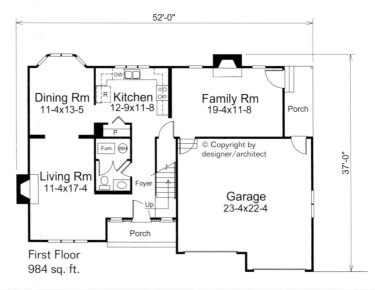

52'-0"

Dining Rm
11-4x13-5

Kitchen
12-9x11-8

Family Rm
19-4x11-8

Porch

Living Rm
11-4x17-4

Foyer

© Copyright by designer/architect

Garage
23-4x22-4

37'-0"

Porch

First Floor
984 sq. ft.

SPECIAL FEATURES

1,285 total square feet of living area

Dining nook creates a warm feeling with a sunny box-bay window

Second floor loft is perfect for a recreation space or office hideaway

Bedrooms include walk-in closets allowing extra storage space

Kitchen, dining and living areas combine making a perfect gathering place

2 bedrooms, 1 bath

Crawl space foundation

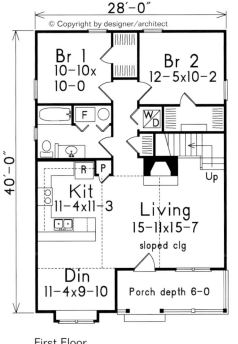

First Floor
1,032 sq. ft.

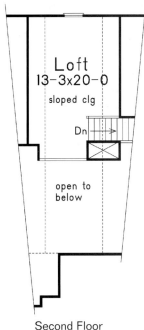

Second Floor
253 sq. ft.

SPECIAL FEATURES

1,974 total square feet of living area

Breakfast room with full windows blends into the family room

Second floor includes private master bedroom suite and easy access to laundry facility

Elegant master bath has a large corner tub with separate shower and vanities

Traditional entrance framed by a covered porch and sidelights

3 bedrooms, 2 1/2 baths, 2-car drive under garage

Basement foundation

Second Floor
976 sq. ft.

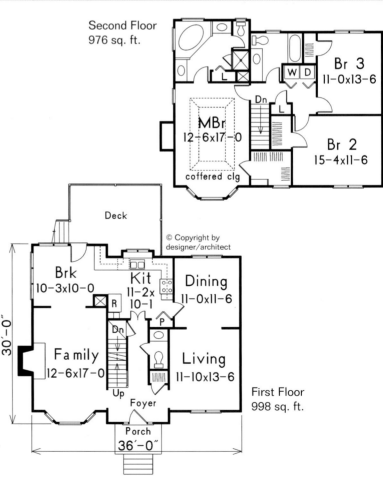

© Copyright by
designer/architect

First Floor
998 sq. ft.

SPECIAL FEATURES

1,390 total square feet of living area

The kitchen with snack bar opens to the spacious great room with plenty of space for dining

A corner fireplace warms the adjoining great room and kitchen

The master bedroom is a relaxing retreat with a private bath and deck access

The secondary bedrooms are separated from the master bedroom and share a full bath

3 bedrooms, 2 baths, 2-car side entry garage

Basement foundation, drawings also include walk-out basement foundation

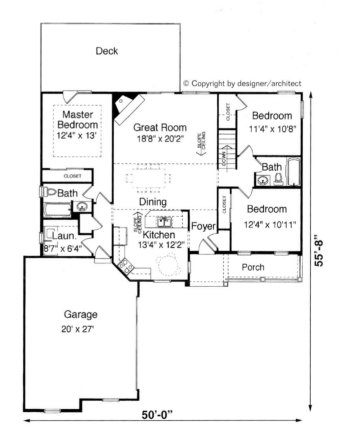

© Copyright by designer/architect

Deck

Master Bedroom 12'4" x 13'

Great Room 18'8" x 20'2"

SLOPE CEILING

Bedroom 11'4" x 10'8"

CLOSET

Bath

Bath

Dining

Bedroom 12'4" x 10'11"

Laun. 8'7" x 6'4"

Kitchen 13'4" x 12'2"

Foyer

Porch

Garage 20' x 27'

55'-8"

50'-0"

SPECIAL FEATURES

1,836 total square feet of living area

Foyer sparkles with spiral stair, a sloped ceiling and celestial windows

Living room enjoys fireplace with bookshelves and view to the outdoors

U-shaped kitchen includes eat-in breakfast area and dining nearby

Master bedroom revels in having a balcony overlooking the living room, a large walk-in closet and private bath

3 bedrooms, 2 1/2 baths

Crawl space foundation, drawings also include slab foundation

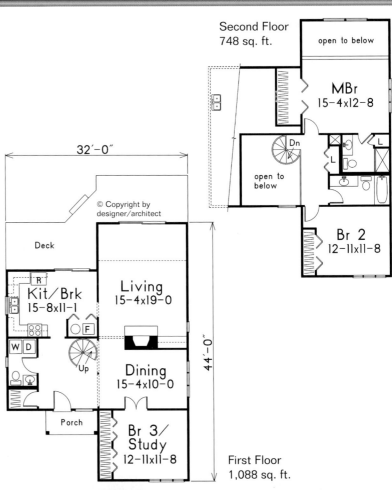

Second Floor 748 sq. ft.

First Floor 1,088 sq. ft.

Lowe's LEGACY SERIES

SPECIAL FEATURES

- 676 total square feet of living area
- Energy efficient home with 2" x 6" exterior walls
- See-through fireplace between bedroom and living area adds character
- Combined dining and living areas create an open feeling
- Full-length front covered porch is perfect for enjoying the outdoors
- Additional storage is available in the utility room
- 1 bedroom, 1 bath
- Crawl space foundation

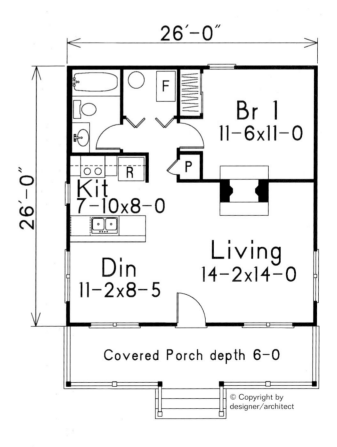

26'-0"

26'-0"

Br 1
11-6x11-0

Kit
7-10x8-0

Din
11-2x8-5

Living
14-2x14-0

Covered Porch depth 6-0

© Copyright by designer/architect

SPECIAL FEATURES

1,800 total square feet of living area

Double doors open into the foyer crowned with a 10' ceiling

The vaulted great room opens into the combined kitchen and bayed breakfast room with decorative columns

The unfinished bonus room has an additional 302 square feet of living area

3 bedrooms, 2 baths, 2-car side entry garage

Slab foundation, drawings also include basement and crawl space foundations

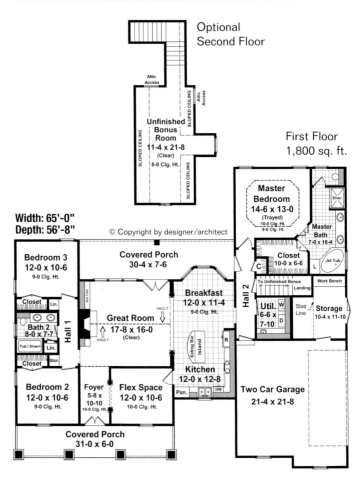

Optional Second Floor

Attic Access

Unfinished Bonus Room
11-4 x 21-8
(Clear)
8-0 Clg. Ht.

SLOPED CEILING

First Floor
1,800 sq. ft.

Width: 65'-0"
Depth: 56'-8"

© Copyright by designer/architect

Master Bedroom
14-6 x 13-0
(Trayed)
10-0 Clg. Ht.
9-0 Clg. Ht.

Master Bath
7-0 x 16-4

Shwr.
Jet Tub

Bedroom 3
12-0 x 10-6
9-0 Clg. Ht.

Covered Porch
30-4 x 7-6

Breakfast
12-0 x 11-4
9-0 Clg. Ht.

Closet
10-0 x 6-6

To Unfinished Bonus
Landing

Work Bench

Closet
Lin.

Hall 1

Hall 2

Util.
6-6 x 7-10

Storage
10-4 x 11-10

Bath 2
8-0 x 7-7

Great Room
17-8 x 16-0
(Clear)
VAULT

Eating Bar
Island

Stair Line

Tub / Shwr.
Lin.

Closet
Stor.

Bedroom 2
12-0 x 10-6
9-0 Clg. Ht.

Foyer
5-8 x 10-10
10-0 Clg. Ht.

Flex Space
12-0 x 10-6
10-0 Clg. Ht.

Kitchen
12-0 x 12-8

Pan.

Two Car Garage
21-4 x 21-8

Covered Porch
31-0 x 6-0

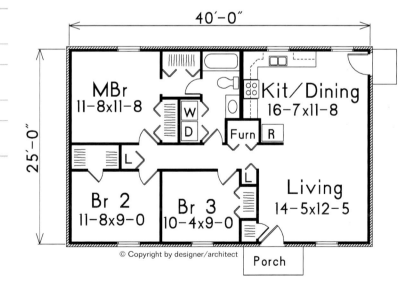

SPECIAL FEATURES

1,000 total square feet of living area

Bath includes convenient
hide-away laundry area

Master bedroom includes double
closets and private access to bath

Foyer features handy coat closet

Kitchen features L-shaped design
and easy access outdoors

3 bedrooms, 1 bath

Crawl space foundation, drawings also
include basement and slab foundations

40'-0"

25'-0"

MBr
11-8x11-8

Kit/Dining
16-7x11-8

W
D

Furn R

Br 2
11-8x9-0

Br 3
10-4x9-0

Living
14-5x12-5

L

L

L

© Copyright by designer/architect

Porch

LOWE'S LEGACY SERIES

SPECIAL FEATURES

2,012 total square feet of living area

Gables, cantilevers, and box-bay windows all contribute to an elegant exterior

Two-story entry leads to an efficient kitchen and bayed breakfast area with morning room

Garage contains extra space for a shop, bicycles and miscellaneous storage

5 bedrooms, 2 1/2 baths, 2-car garage

Basement foundation

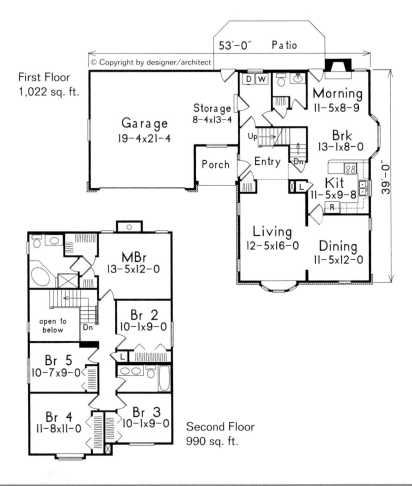

First Floor
1,022 sq. ft.

© Copyright by designer/architect

53'-0"   Patio

Garage
19-4x21-4

Storage
8-4x13-4

Morning
11-5x8-9

Brk
13-1x8-0

Porch

Up

Entry

Dn

Kit
11-5x9-8

39'-0"

Living
12-5x16-0

Dining
11-5x12-0

MBr
13-5x12-0

Br 2
10-1x9-0

open to
below   Dn

Br 5
10-7x9-0

Br 4
11-8x11-0

Br 3
10-1x9-0

Second Floor
990 sq. ft.

SPECIAL FEATURES

2,206 total square feet of living area

Energy efficient home with
2" x 6" exterior walls

The vaulted second floor master bedroom
has an expansive walk-in closet and
a private bath with a whirlpool tub

The secondary bedrooms share a well
designed bath with the toilet and tub
separated from the sink by a pocket door

The second floor laundry room
makes this household chore
convenient to all the bedrooms

3 bedrooms, 2 1/2 baths, 3-car garage

Basement foundation

Second Floor
1,120 sq. ft.

Br. 3
12-1x11-11

MBr.
13-6x16-7
Vaulted Clg

Br. 2
13-4x11-2

First Floor
1,086 sq. ft.

Kit.
12-9X11-9

Breakfast
12-5x9-9

Family
13-6x15-6

Mud

Dining
13-6x11-6

Porch

Garage
31-4x23-2

9x7 Door   16x7 Door

45'-8"

62'-0"

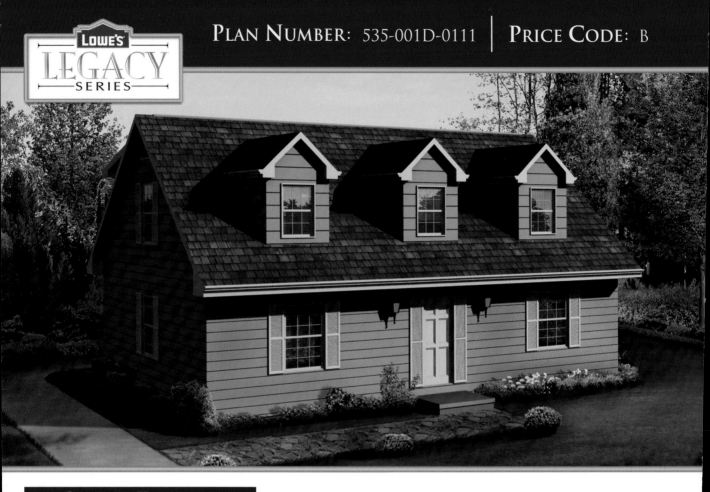

SPECIAL FEATURES

1,772 total square feet of living area

Energy efficient home with
2" x 6" exterior walls

Cozy design with two bedrooms on
the first floor and two bedrooms on
the second floor for added privacy

L-shaped kitchen provides easy access
to the dining room and the outdoors

Convenient first floor laundry area

4 bedrooms, 2 baths

Crawl space foundation, drawings also
include basement and slab foundations

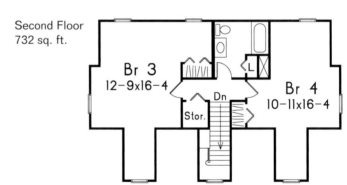

Second Floor
732 sq. ft.

Br 3
12-9x16-4

Br 4
10-11x16-4

Dn

Stor.

L

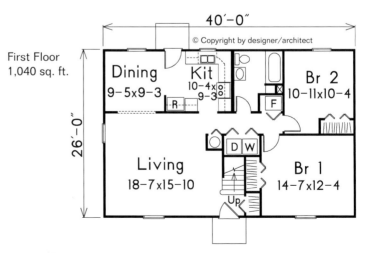

First Floor
1,040 sq. ft.

40'-0"

© Copyright by designer/architect

26'-0"

Dining
9-5x9-3

Kit
10-4x
9-3

Br 2
10-11x10-4

R

F

Living
18-7x15-10

D W

Br 1
14-7x12-4

Up

SPECIAL FEATURES

960 total square feet of living area

Attractive appearance adds
to any neighborhood

A nice-sized living room leads to an informal
family area with eat-in L-shaped kitchen,
access to rear yard and basement space

Three bedrooms with lots of
closet space and a convenient
hall bath complete the home

3 bedrooms, 1 bath

Basement foundation, drawings also
include crawl space and slab foundations

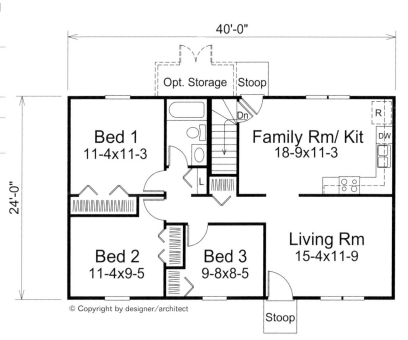

© Copyright by designer/architect

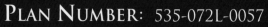

SPECIAL FEATURES

1,800 total square feet of living area

This Craftsman style home features a stylish exterior and amenity-full interior

Cheerful and bright, the family room is the perfect place to relax and will no doubt be the center of activity

Substantial closet space can be found in the remotely located master suite

3 bedrooms, 2 baths, 2-car rear entry garage

Basement foundation

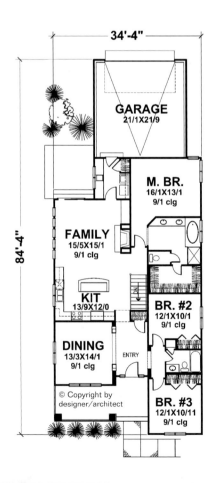

SPECIAL FEATURES

2,046 total square feet of living area

Hipped roof and special brickwork provide nice curb appeal

The kitchen and breakfast room offer island cabinetry, a walk-in pantry, a wide bay window and easy access to a large dining room

Cheery transom windows and fireplace are just two amenities of the huge great room

The second floor has large secondary bedrooms and a spacious master bedroom with a double-door entry, double walk-in closets and a luxury bath with corner tub

4 bedrooms, 2 1/2 baths, 2-car garage

Basement foundation

Second Floor
1,015 sq. ft.

Br 3
11-0x11-0

Br 2
9-6x10-0

Dn

Br 4
13-4x11-7

MBr
13-0x16-11

coffered clg.

37'-0"

Patio

Brk fst.
10-6x14-1

Kitchen
10-6x12-1

R

P

Great Room
13-4x21-6

Dn

D W S

Up

Entry

Dining
17-4x11-0

tray clg.

49'-8"

Porch depth 5-4

© Copyright by designer/architect

Garage
19-4x20-4

First Floor
1,031 sq. ft.

LOWE'S LEGACY SERIES

SPECIAL FEATURES

1,818 total square feet of living area

Energy efficient home with
2" x 6" exterior walls

Spacious living and dining rooms

Master bedroom features large bay,
walk-in closet, dressing area and bath

Convenient carport and storage area

3 bedrooms, 2 1/2 baths

Crawl space foundation, drawings also
include basement and slab foundations

First Floor
928 sq. ft.

Second Floor
890 sq. ft.

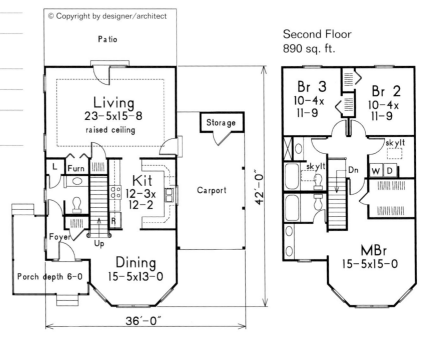

© Copyright by designer/architect

Patio

Living
23-5x15-8
raised ceiling

Storage

L | Furn

Kit
12-3x
12-2

Carport

Foyer

Up

Dining
15-5x13-0

Porch depth 6-0

36'-0"

42'-0"

Br 3
10-4x
11-9

Br 2
10-4x
11-9

skylt

skylt

Dn

W D

MBr
15-5x15-0

SPECIAL FEATURES

568 total square feet of living area

A covered entry welcomes guests into this delightful garage apartment

Beautiful dormers brighten the interior

The kitchen counter overlooks the sitting area for efficiency

1 bedroom, 1 bath, 2-car garage

Basement foundation

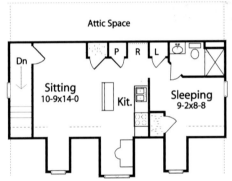

Attic Space

Dn

P R L

Sitting
10-9x14-0

Kit.

Sleeping
9-2x8-8

Second Floor
568 sq. ft.

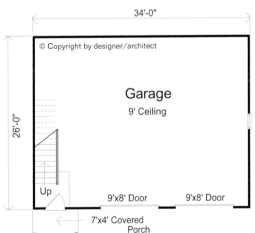

34'-0"

© Copyright by designer/architect

First Floor

Garage
9' Ceiling

26'-0"

Up

9'x8' Door

9'x8' Door

7'x4' Covered
Porch

SPECIAL FEATURES

1,834 total square feet of living area

This attractive European-inspired home is designed especially for today's narrow lots and offers a well-planned interior

Tucked into the back of this home you'll find a family room with double French doors leading onto a deck

A cozy fireplace can be enjoyed from the family room, breakfast nook and kitchen

3 bedrooms, 2 1/2 baths, 2-car garage

Basement foundation

Rear View

Second Floor
933 sq. ft.

VAULT   VAULT   LINEN

MASTER BEDROOM
16'-1" x 13'-0"   SHOWER

CLOSET
6'-5" x 6'-7"   BEDROOM 2
12'-8" x 11'-6"

LAUNDRY   LINEN

OPEN
BELOW   BEDROOM 3
10'-0" x 13'-3"

DECK
16'-4" x 11'-8"

NOOK
8'-4" x 13'-0"

KITCHEN
9'-2" x 13'-0"   FLOOR
DROPS 6"

PANTRY   FAMILY
16'-4" x 15'-0"

CRAWL
OR SLAB   COATS
DOOR
LOCATION   38'-0"

UP

BASEMENT
DOOR
LOCATION   GARAGE
18'-0" x 19'-0"

DINING
10'-8" x 16'-0"

© Copyright by
designer/architect

First Floor
901 sq. ft.

35'-0"

SPECIAL FEATURES

1,922 total square feet of living area

Master bedroom includes many luxuries such as an oversized private bath and large walk-in closet

The kitchen is spacious with a functional eat-in breakfast bar and is adjacent to the nook which is ideal as a breakfast room

Plenty of storage is featured in both bedrooms on the second floor and in the hall

Enormous utility room is centrally located on the first floor

3 bedrooms, 2 1/2 baths

Basement foundation

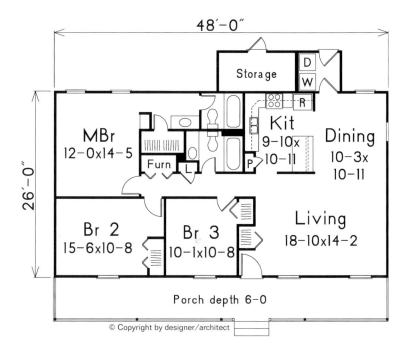

SPECIAL FEATURES

1,285 total square feet of living area

Energy efficient home with
2" x 6" exterior walls

Accommodating home with ranch style porch

Large storage area

Master bedroom includes dressing area,
private bath and built-in bookcase

Kitchen features pantry, breakfast bar
and complete view to dining room

3 bedrooms, 2 baths

Crawl space foundation, drawings also
include basement and slab foundations

© Copyright by designer/architect

SPECIAL FEATURES

1,568 total square feet of living area

Family and friends will love to gather around the kitchen snack bar that is open to the dining and great rooms

A half bath, walk-in pantry and laundry area at the garage entrance adds simplicity to family functions

A vaulted ceiling crowns the master bedroom, and the deluxe bath makes this area a luxurious suite

3 bedrooms, 2 1/2 baths, 2-car garage

Basement foundation

50'-0"

50'-4"

Dining
9-4x11-6
Vaulted

Great Room
15-11x14-9
Vaulted

MBr
13-2x14-6
Vaulted

Kitchen
10-6x11-6
Vaulted

D

R

Dn

L

D
W
S Laun.

P

Br 2
10-4x11-0

Br 3
11-0x10-7

Garage
19-4x19-4

Covered
Porch

© Copyright by
designer/architect

Special Features

1,983 total square feet of living area

Second floor balcony overlooks first floor adding spaciousness

Traditional styling with a contemporary interior flair

Isolated first floor master bedroom suite for privacy

Secondary bedrooms both have large walk-in closets

3 bedrooms, 2 1/2 baths, 2-car drive under garage

Basement foundation

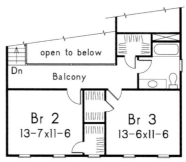

open to below

Dn

Balcony

Br 2
13-7x11-6

Br 3
13-6x11-6

Second Floor
584 sq. ft.

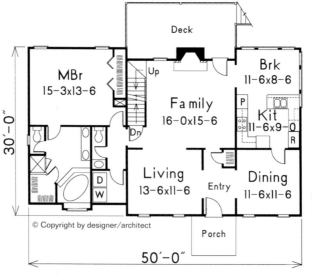

Deck

MBr
15-3x13-6

Up

Brk
11-6x8-6

Family
16-0x15-6

P

Kit
11-6x9-0

R

Dn

D
W

Living
13-6x11-6

Entry

Dining
11-6x11-6

© Copyright by designer/architect

Porch

30'-0"

50'-0"

First Floor
1,399 sq. ft.

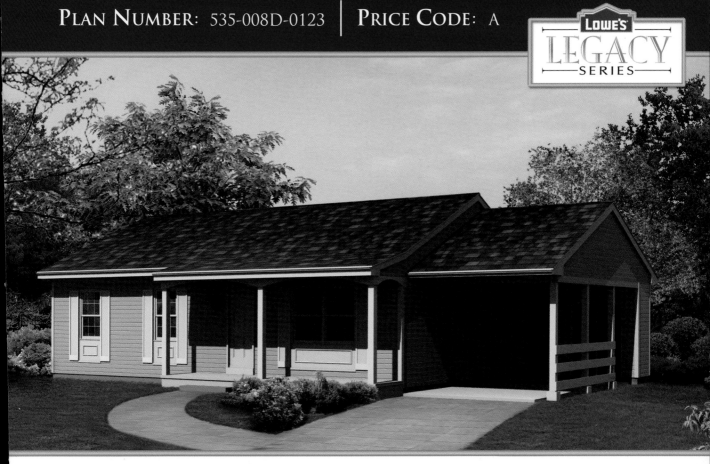

SPECIAL FEATURES

1,120 total square feet of living area

Energy efficient home with
2" x 6" exterior walls

Porch and shuttered windows
with lower accent panels add
greatly to this home's appeal

Kitchen offers a snack counter
and opens to the family room

All bedrooms provide excellent closet space

Carport includes building for ample storage

3 bedrooms, 1 1/2 baths, 1-car carport

Basement foundation, drawings also
include crawl space and slab foundations

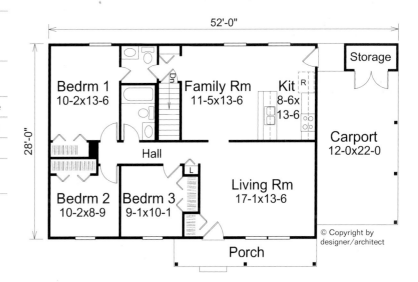

© Copyright by
designer/architect

SPECIAL FEATURES

1,516 total square feet of living area

On the second floor the stairway looks out over the living room

Master bedroom enjoys first floor privacy and a luxurious bath

Kitchen has easy access to the deck, laundry closet and garage

3 bedrooms, 2 1/2 baths, 2-car garage

Basement foundation

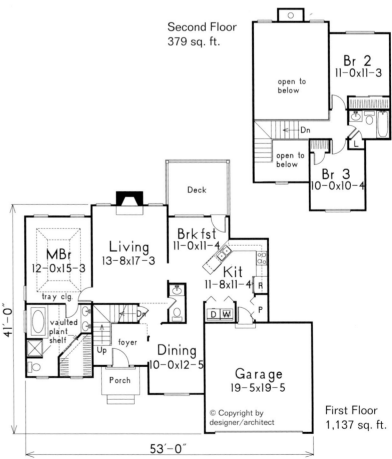

Second Floor
379 sq. ft.

Br 2
11-0x11-3

open to below

Dn

open to below

Br 3
10-0x10-4

Deck

Brkfst
11-0x11-4

MBr
12-0x15-3

Living
13-8x17-3

Kit
11-8x11-4

tray clg.

vaulted plant shelf

Up

foyer

Dining
10-0x12-5

Porch

Garage
19-5x19-5

© Copyright by designer/architect

41'-0"

53'-0"

First Floor
1,137 sq. ft.

SPECIAL FEATURES

1,993 total square feet of living area

This superb ranch features an open living area with split-bedrooms

An eating bar extends the kitchen connecting it to the breakfast area and family room

The massive master bedroom enjoys a walk-in closet and luxurious bath

3 bedrooms, 2 baths, 2-car garage

Basement foundation

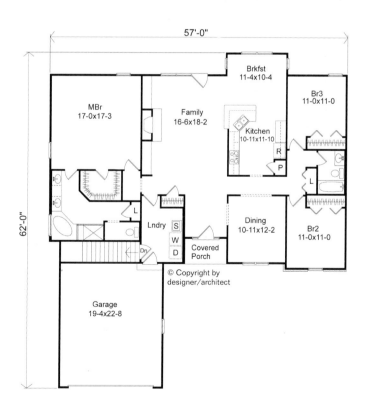

© Copyright by designer/architect

Lowe's
LEGACY
SERIES

SPECIAL FEATURES

1,887 total square feet of living area

Varied ceiling heights throughout create an exciting interior

A roomy breakfast area is open to the kitchen and has direct access outdoors onto the rear porch

The master bath enjoys a tub, separate shower and double-bowl vanity

The optional second floor has an additional 263 square feet of living area

3 bedrooms, 2 baths, 2-car garage

Basement foundation

Attic

Stairs Down

Optional
Second Floor

Sloped Clg.
Sloped Clg.

Optional Bonus
11/3 x 23/5
8' Clg.

© Copyright by designer/architect

Rear Porch
13/4 x 8

Master
17 x 13/8
9' Clg.

Breakfast
13/4 x 12/2
Desk
9' Clg.

8/7 x 12/1
Bath #1

Snack Bar

Family Room
19/4 x 16
14' Clg.

Kitchen
9/4 x 15/2

Pantry

Bedroom #2
12/8 x 11
9' Clg.

Sloped Clg.

Sloped Clg.

Stairs Up
Stairs Down

8' Clg.

W D

Bath #2

Foyer
6 x 10/9

8' Clg.

Bedroom #3
12/8 x 11

Dining
11 x 12/9
9' Clg.

Garage
21/5 x 23/5

Stoop

First Floor
1,887 sq. ft.

Width: 60'-9"
Depth: 58'-1"

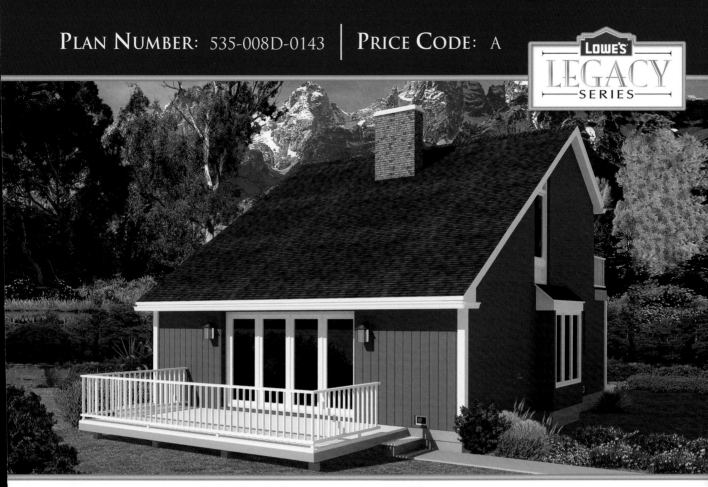

LOWE'S LEGACY SERIES

SPECIAL FEATURES

1,299 total square feet of living area

Convenient storage for skis, etc. is located outside the front entrance

The kitchen and dining room receive light from the box-bay window

Large vaulted living room features a cozy fireplace and overlook from the second floor balcony

Two second floor bedrooms share a Jack and Jill bath

Second floor balcony extends over the entire length of the living room below

3 bedrooms, 2 baths

Crawl space foundation, drawings also include slab foundation

First Floor
811 sq. ft.

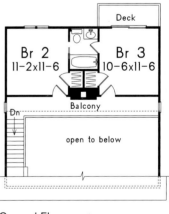

Second Floor
488 sq. ft.

SPECIAL FEATURES

1,428 total square feet of living area

Energy efficient home with
2" x 6" exterior walls

10' ceilings in the entry and hallway

Vaulted secondary bedrooms

Kitchen is loaded with amenities including
an island with salad sink and pantry

Master bedroom with vaulted
ceiling includes a large walk-in
closet and private master bath

3 bedrooms, 2 baths, 2-car garage

Basement foundation, drawings also
include crawl space foundation

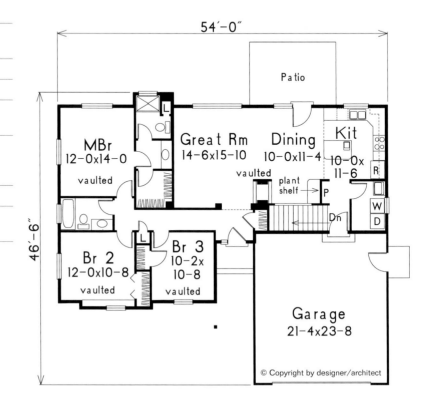

© Copyright by designer/architect

Lowe's LEGACY SERIES

SPECIAL FEATURES

952 total square feet of living area

Kitchen/breakfast area includes island ideal for food preparation or dining

Spacious bath directly accesses the bedroom as well as the sitting area

Laundry area on the lower level gives this apartment all the conveniences of home

1 bedroom, 1 bath, 2-car garage

Slab foundation

Second Floor
952 sq. ft.

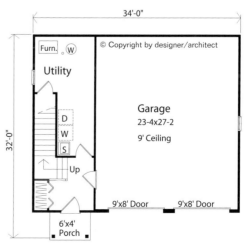

First Floor

© Copyright by designer/architect

SPECIAL FEATURES

2,058 total square feet of living area

Designed for today's more narrow lots, this home adds style to any neighborhood

All bedrooms are located on the second floor but are easily accessible thanks to a centrally located elevator

The dramatic and spacious kitchen flows neatly from an angled pantry to the recipe desk and serving bar

3 bedrooms, 2 1/2 baths, 2-car garage

Slab foundation, drawings also include crawl space foundation

Rear View

First Floor
1,135 sq. ft.

© Copyright by designer/architect

DECK
26'-5" x 9'-8"

BREAKFAST
8'-10" x 12'-10"

FAMILY
17'-2" x 14'-1"

KITCHEN
13'-2 x 18'-6"

ELEVATOR
2'-11" x 4'-4"

PANTRY

COATS

DINING
11'-0" x 14'-11"

GARAGE
18'-0" x 24'-10"

PORCH
16'-0" x 5'-8"

43'-6"

35'-0"

Second Floor
923 sq. ft.

BEDROOM 3
12'-4" x 11'-4"

HERS

VAULT

VAULT

ELEVATOR

LINEN

BEDROOM 2
11'-0" x 15'-6"

LAUNDRY
8'-1" x 5'-0"

MASTER SUITE
14'-6" x 15'-4"

TRAY CEILING

HIS

SITTING
7'-0" x 9'-2"

BALCONY

LOWE'S
LEGACY
SERIES

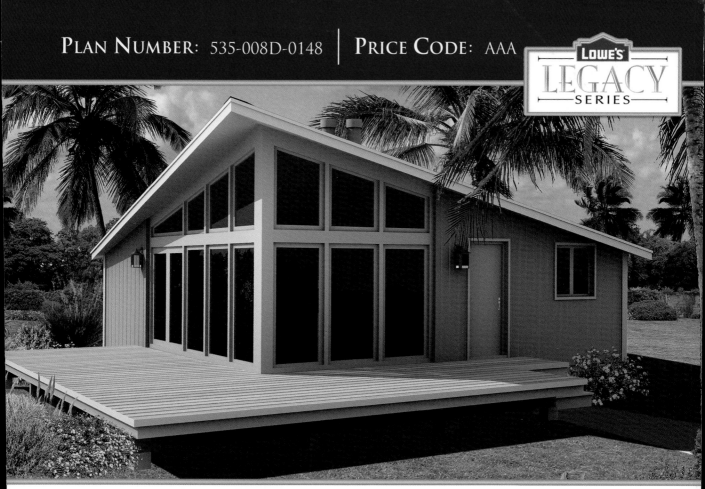

SPECIAL FEATURES

784 total square feet of living area

Outdoor relaxation will be enjoyed with this home's huge wrap-around wood deck

Upon entering the spacious living area, a cozy free-standing fireplace, sloped ceiling and corner window wall catch the eye

Charming kitchen features pass-through peninsula to dining area

3 bedrooms, 1 bath

Pier foundation

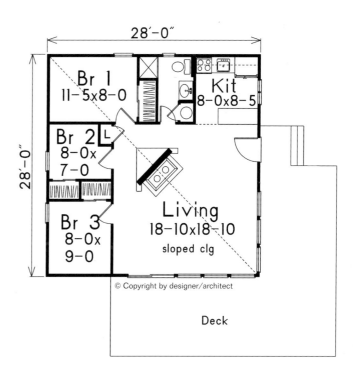

28'-0"

28'-0"

Br 1
11-5x8-0

Kit
8-0x8-5

Br 2
8-0x
7-0

Br 3
8-0x
9-0

Living
18-10x18-10
sloped clg

© Copyright by designer/architect

Deck

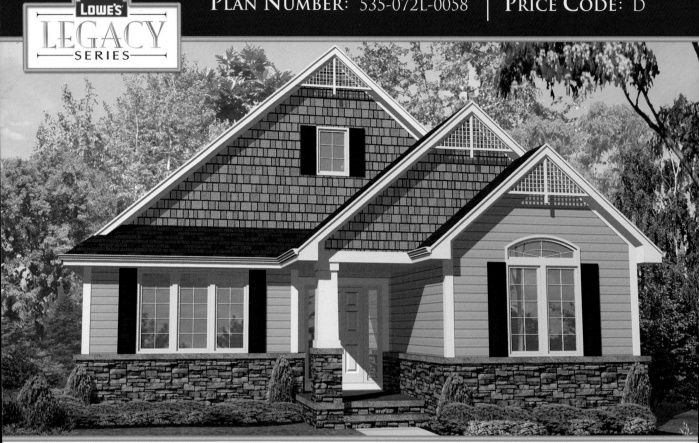

SPECIAL FEATURES

1,800 total square feet of living area

Suited for a narrow lot, this bungalow offers tremendous curb appeal and a stylish interior

An entire wall of windows adds a generous amount of sunlight to the family room

The master bedroom is separated from the other bedrooms and also enjoys a private bath with shower and whirlpool tub

3 bedrooms, 2 baths, 2-car rear entry garage

Basement foundation

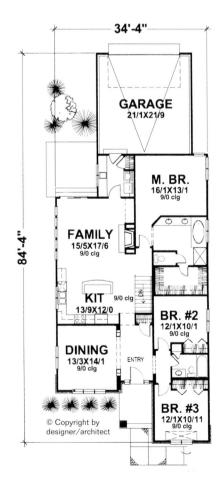

SPECIAL FEATURES

988 total square feet of living area

Great room features a corner fireplace

Vaulted ceiling and corner windows add space and light to the great room

Eat-in kitchen with vaulted ceiling accesses deck for outdoor living

Master bedroom features separate vanities and private access to the bath

2 bedrooms, 1 bath, 2-car garage

Basement foundation

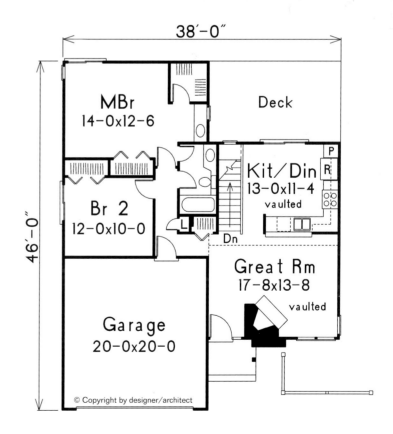

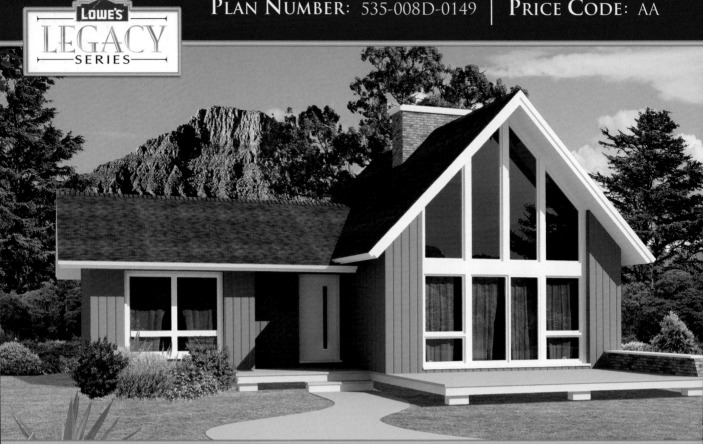

SPECIAL FEATURES

1,160 total square feet of living area

Kitchen/dining area combines with the laundry area creating a functional and organized space

Spacious vaulted living area has a large fireplace and is brightened by glass doors accessing the large deck

Ascend to the second floor loft by spiral stairs and find a cozy hideaway

Master bedroom is brightened by many windows and includes a private bath and double closets

1 bedroom, 1 bath

Crawl space foundation

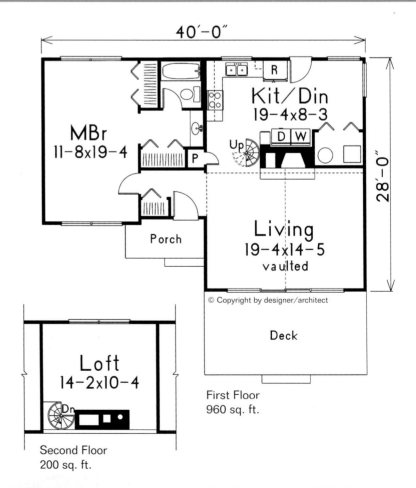

40'-0"

28'-0"

Kit/Din
19-4x8-3

MBr
11-8x19-4

Up

D W

Porch

Living
19-4x14-5
vaulted

© Copyright by designer/architect

Deck

First Floor
960 sq. ft.

Loft
14-2x10-4

Dn

Second Floor
200 sq. ft.

LEGACY
SERIES

SPECIAL FEATURES

868 total square feet of living area

Large utility room adds convenience
to this garage apartment

The dining and great rooms flow together

The kitchen features a snack bar counter

1 bedroom, 1 bath, 2-car garage

Basement foundation

31'-0"

Kitchen
8'-4"x9'

Dining
13'x11'

28'-0"

Mast. Bed
13'-4x12'

Great Room
16'x13'

Second Floor
868 sq. ft.

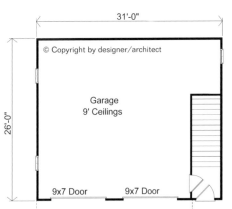

31'-0"

© Copyright by designer/architect

Garage
9' Ceilings

26'-0"

9x7 Door   9x7 Door

First Floor

SPECIAL FEATURES

1,093 total square feet of living area

The lovely master bedroom has two corner windows making it ideal for furniture placement and a vaulted private bath

The washer and dryer are located directly off the kitchen for quick and easy access

The symmetrically designed family room has a center fireplace flanked on each side by sunny windows

3 bedrooms, 2 baths, 2-car garage

Slab foundation, drawings also include basement foundation

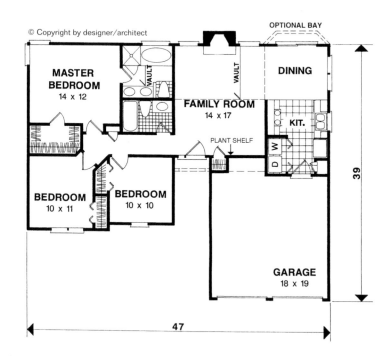

© Copyright by designer/architect

OPTIONAL BAY

MASTER BEDROOM
14 x 12

VAULT

DINING

VAULT

FAMILY ROOM
14 x 17

KIT.

PLANT SHELF

W   D

BEDROOM
10 x 11

BEDROOM
10 x 10

GARAGE
18 x 19

39

47

SPECIAL FEATURES

1,539 total square feet of living area

Standard 9' ceilings

Master bedroom features a 10'
tray ceiling, access to porch, ample
closet space and a full bath

Serving counter separates
kitchen and dining room

Foyer with handy coat closet opens
to living area with fireplace

Handy utility room near kitchen

3 bedrooms, 2 baths, 2-car garage

Slab foundation

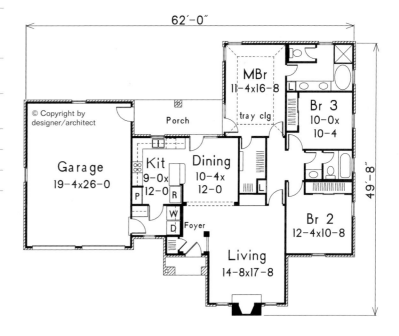

Lowe's LEGACY SERIES

SPECIAL FEATURES

665 total square feet of living area

Spacious breakfast/sitting area flows into the kitchen

A stacked washer and dryer adds convenience to this cottage home

A coat closet at the entry and a pantry in the kitchen provide essential storage space

1 bedroom, 1 bath, 1-car garage

Slab foundation

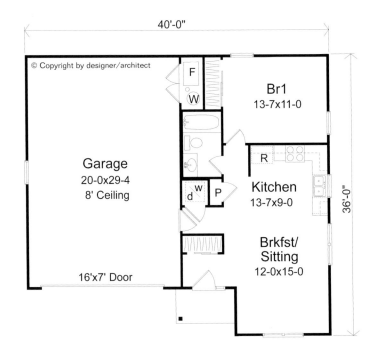

40'-0"

© Copyright by designer/architect

F
W

Br1
13-7x11-0

Garage
20-0x29-4
8' Ceiling

R

Kitchen
13-7x9-0

w d   P

36'-0"

Brkfst/
Sitting
12-0x15-0

16'x7' Door

SPECIAL FEATURES

2,024 total square feet of living area

Impressive fireplace and sloped
ceiling in the family room

Master bedroom features a vaulted ceiling,
separate dressing room and a walk-in closet

Breakfast area includes a work
desk and accesses the deck

4 bedrooms, 2 1/2 baths,
2-car side entry garage

Basement foundation

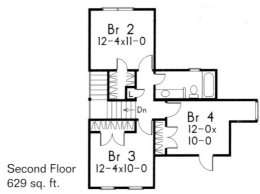

Br 2
12-4x11-0

Br 4
12-0x
10-0

Br 3
12-4x10-0

Dn

Second Floor
629 sq. ft.

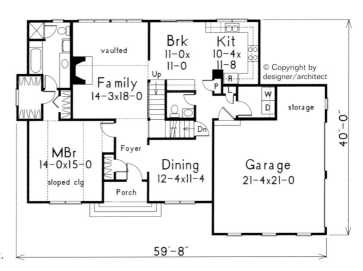

Brk
11-0x
11-0

Kit
10-4x
11-8

vaulted

Family
14-3x18-0

© Copyright by
designer/architect

Up

storage

W
D

MBr
14-0x15-0

sloped clg

Foyer

Dining
12-4x11-4

Garage
21-4x21-0

Porch

Dn

40'-0"

First Floor
1,395 sq. ft.

59'-8"

SPECIAL FEATURES

1,312 total square feet of living area

Expansive deck extends directly off living area

L-shaped kitchen is organized and efficient

Bedroom to the left of the kitchen makes a great quiet retreat or office

Living area is flanked with windows for light

3 bedrooms, 1 bath

Pier foundation

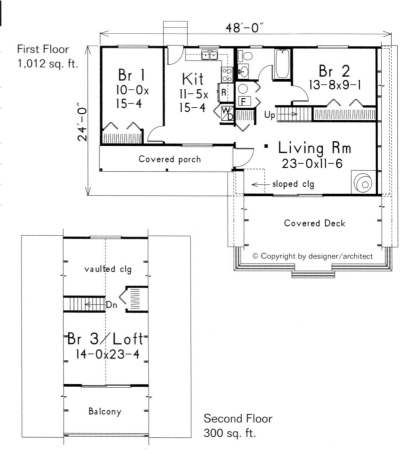

First Floor
1,012 sq. ft.

48'-0"

24'-0"

Br 1
10-0x
15-4

Kit
11-5x
15-4

R

F

W/D

Br 2
13-8x9-1

Up

Covered porch

Living Rm
23-0x11-6

sloped clg

Covered Deck

© Copyright by designer/architect

vaulted clg

Dn

Br 3/Loft
14-0x23-4

Balcony

Second Floor
300 sq. ft.

SPECIAL FEATURES

1,824 total square feet of living area

Living room features a 10' ceiling, fireplace and media center

Dining room includes a bay window and convenient kitchen access

Master bedroom features a large walk-in closet and luxurious bath with a double-door entry

Modified U-shaped kitchen features pantry and bar

3 bedrooms, 2 baths, 2-car detached garage

Slab foundation

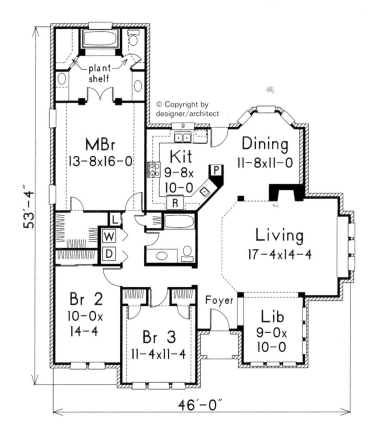

plant shelf

© Copyright by designer/architect

MBr
13-8x16-0

Kit
9-8x
10-0

Dining
11-8x11-0

P

R

Living
17-4x14-4

L

W

D

Br 2
10-0x
14-4

Br 3
11-4x11-4

Foyer

Lib
9-0x
10-0

53'-4"

46'-0"

SPECIAL FEATURES

1,498 total square feet of living area

The great room with a gas fireplace and sloped ceiling is visible from the foyer, dining room and kitchen creating a large, open gathering area

The master bedroom enjoys a luxurious bath, large walk-in closet and raised ceiling

A snack bar, walk-in pantry and nearby laundry room enhance the spacious kitchen

Two generously sized bedrooms share a full bath with convenient linen closet

3 bedrooms, 2 baths, 2-car garage

Basement foundation, drawings also include slab and crawl space foundations

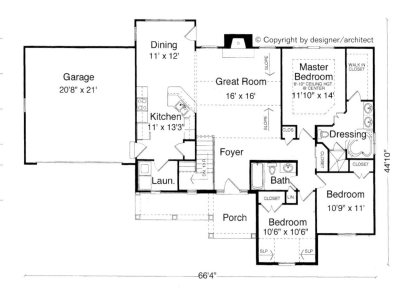

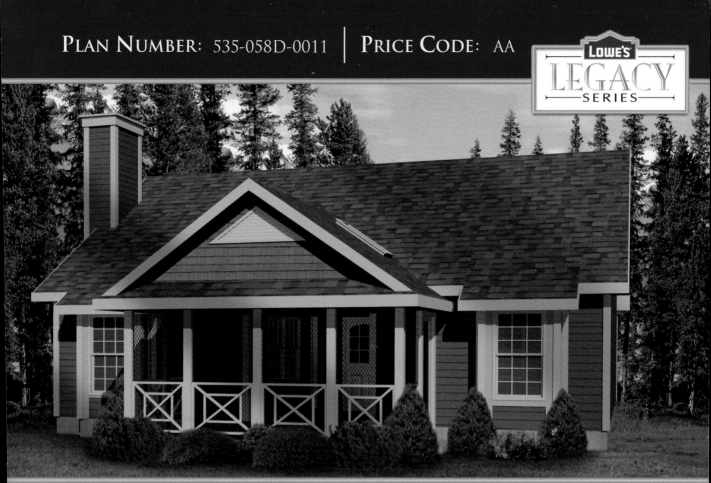

LOWE'S LEGACY SERIES

SPECIAL FEATURES

924 total square feet of living area

Box-bay window seats brighten the interior while enhancing the front facade

Spacious kitchen with lots of cabinet space and a large pantry

T-shaped covered porch is screened for added enjoyment

Plenty of closet space throughout with linen closets in both bedrooms

2 bedrooms, 1 bath

Slab foundation

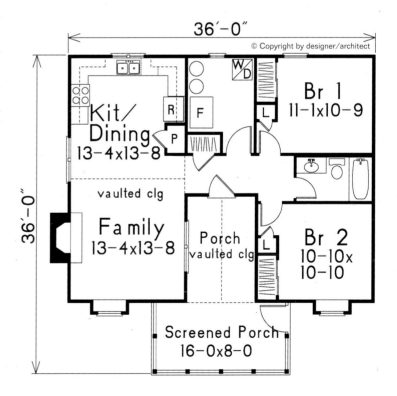

36'-0"

© Copyright by designer/architect

36'-0"

Kit/Dining
13-4x13-8

vaulted clg

Family
13-4x13-8

Porch
vaulted clg

Br 1
11-1x10-9

Br 2
10-10x
10-10

Screened Porch
16-0x8-0

SPECIAL FEATURES

2,200 total square feet of living area

Step inside this inviting home to find an exquisite great room topped with a tray ceiling and featuring a gas fireplace flanked by built-in shelves

The nearby kitchen is centrally located, offering a walk-in pantry and raised snack bar, and easily serves both the formal dining room and the casual breakfast area

The master bedroom pampers with two walk-in closets and a compartmented bath equipped with a jet tub and twin vanity

The optional second floor has an additional 371 square feet of living area

4 bedrooms, 2 1/2 baths, 2-car side entry garage

Crawl space foundation, drawings also include slab foundation

Optional Second Floor

First Floor
2,200 sq. ft.

Width: 65'-6"
Depth: 79'-6"

LOWE'S LEGACY SERIES

SPECIAL FEATURES

1,705 total square feet of living area

Energy efficient home with 2" x 6" exterior walls

Two bedrooms on the first floor for convenience and two bedrooms on the second floor for privacy

L-shaped kitchen adjacent to dining room accesses the outdoors

First floor laundry area

4 bedrooms, 2 baths

Crawl space foundation, drawings also include basement and slab foundations

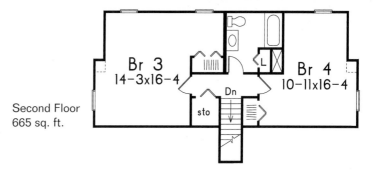

Second Floor
665 sq. ft.

Br 3
14-3x16-4

Br 4
10-11x16-4

Dn

sto

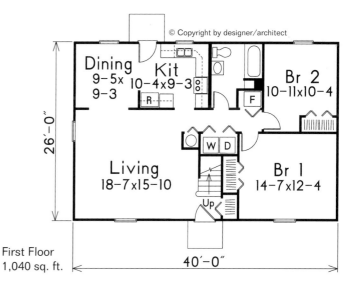

© Copyright by designer/architect

Dining
9-5x 9-3

Kit
10-4x9-3

Br 2
10-11x10-4

26'-0"

Living
18-7x15-10

W D

Br 1
14-7x12-4

Up

First Floor
1,040 sq. ft.

40'-0"

SPECIAL FEATURES

1,428 total square feet of living area

Energy efficient home with
2" x 6" exterior walls

Large vaulted family room opens to the
dining area and kitchen with breakfast bar

First floor master bedroom offers
a large bath, walk-in closet and
nearby laundry facilities

A spacious loft/bedroom #3 overlooking
the family room and an additional bedroom
and bath complement the second floor

3 bedrooms, 2 baths

Basement foundation

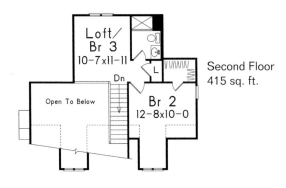

Loft/
Br 3
10-7x11-11

Dn

Open To Below

Br 2
12-8x10-0

Second Floor
415 sq. ft.

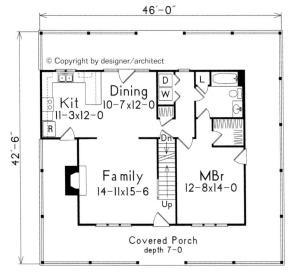

46'-0"

© Copyright by designer/architect

42'-6"

Kit
11-3x12-0

Dining
10-7x12-0

D
W

Dn

Family
14-11x15-6

Up

MBr
12-8x14-0

First Floor
1,013 sq. ft.

Covered Porch
depth 7-0

SPECIAL FEATURES

1,672 total square feet of living area

Energy efficient home with
2" x 6" exterior walls

Foyer opens to a grand living
room with fireplace

The kitchen and dining room combine
for a comfortable living area and
feature access to the outdoors

The elegant master bedroom
features a deluxe bath with a
walk-in closet and whirlpool tub

4 bedrooms, 2 1/2 baths, 2-car garage

Basement foundation

Second Floor
610 sq. ft.

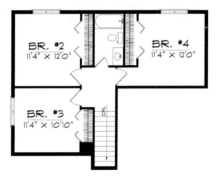

First Floor
1,062 sq. ft.

© Copyright by
designer/architect

LOWE'S
LEGACY
SERIES

SPECIAL FEATURES

2,167 total square feet of living area

Multi-gables with window shutters and plant boxes combined with stone veneer, create an elegant country facade

L-shaped kitchen has work island snack bar open to bayed breakfast room and large family room to provide a 40' vista

Entry and breakfast room access second floor via T-stair

Vaulted master bedroom has a walk-in closet adjacent to luxury master bath

4 bedrooms, 2 1/2 baths, 2-car garage

Basement foundation

First Floor
1,032 sq. ft.

40'-0"

Patio

Kitchen
11-2x13-0

Brk fst
9-10x12-9

Family Rm
18-4x15-9

R

Pantry

Up

Dining
12-0x13-0

Up

Entry

Dn

W D

Laundry

45'-8"

Porch

Garage
20-4x21-4

© Copyright by
designer/architect

Br 3
12-0x10-4

Br 2
10-5x10-4

MBr
14-0x16-0
vaulted

L

L

Dn

Br 4
12-0x12-3

vault

Second Floor
1,135 sq. ft.

SPECIAL FEATURES

1,618 total square feet of living area

Wrap-around porch offers a covered passageway to the garage

Dramatic two-story entry, with balcony above and staircase provide an expansive feel with an added decorative oval window

Dazzling kitchen features walk-in pantry, convenient laundry and covered rear porch

3 bedrooms, 2 1/2 baths, 1-car garage

Basement foundation

Second Floor
754 sq. ft.

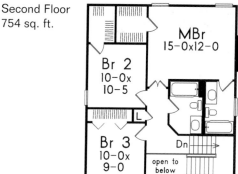

MBr
15-0x12-0

Br 2
10-0x
10-5

Br 3
10-0x
9-0

L

Dn

open to below

50'-4"

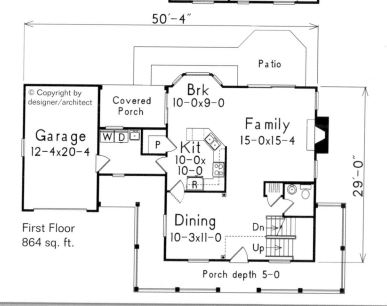

Patio

Brk
10-0x9-0

© Copyright by designer/architect

Covered Porch

Family
15-0x15-4

Garage
12-4x20-4

W D

P

Kit
10-0x
10-0

R

29'-0"

Dining
10-3x11-0

Dn

Up

First Floor
864 sq. ft.

Porch depth 5-0

OUR BLUEPRINT PACKAGES INCLUDE...

Quality plans for building your future, with extras that provide unsurpassed value, ensure good construction and long-term enjoyment.

COVER SHEET

Included with many of the plans, the cover sheet is the artist's rendering of the exterior of the home. It will give you an idea of how your home will look when completed and landscaped.

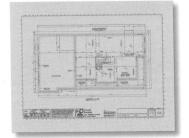

FOUNDATION

The foundation plan shows the layout of the basement, walk-out basement, crawl space, slab or pier foundation. All necessary notations and dimensions are included. See plan page for the foundation types included. If the home plan you choose does not have your desired foundation type, our Customer Service Representatives can advise you on how to customize your foundation to suit your specific needs or site conditions.

FLOOR PLANS

The floor plans show the placement of walls, doors, closets, plumbing fixtures, electrical outlets, columns, and beams for each level of the home.

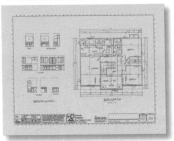

INTERIOR ELEVATIONS

Interior elevations provide views of special interior elements such as fireplaces, kitchen cabinets, built-in units and other features of the home.

EXTERIOR ELEVATIONS

Exterior elevations illustrate the front, rear and both sides of the house, with all details of exterior materials and the required dimensions.

SECTIONS

Show detail views of the home or portions of the home as if it were sliced from the roof to the foundation. This sheet shows important areas such as load-bearing walls, stairs, joists, trusses and other structural elements, which are critical for proper construction.

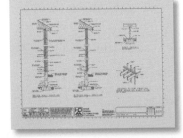

DETAILS

Show how to construct certain components of your home, such as the roof system, stairs, deck, etc.

Now that you've found the home you've been looking for, here are some suggestions on how to make your Dream Home a reality. To get started, order the type of plans that fit your particular situation.

YOUR CHOICES

THE ONE-SET STUDY PACKAGE -

We offer a One-set plan package so you can study your home in detail. This one set is considered a study set and is marked "not for construction." It is a copyright violation to reproduce blueprints.

THE MINIMUM 5-SET PACKAGE -

If you're ready to start the construction process, this 5-set package is the minimum number of blueprint sets you will need. It will require keeping close track of each set so they can be used by multiple subcontractors and tradespeople.

THE STANDARD 8-SET PACKAGE -

For best results in terms of cost, schedule and quality of construction, we recommend you order eight (or more) sets of blueprints. Besides one set for yourself, additional sets of blueprints will be required by your mortgage lender, local building department, general contractor and all subcontractors working on foundation, electrical, plumbing, heating/air conditioning, carpentry work, etc.

REPRODUCIBLE MASTERS -

If you wish to make some minor design changes, you'll want to order reproducible masters. These drawings contain the same information as the blueprints. They are easy to alter and clearly indicate your right to copy or reproduce. This will allow your builder or a local design professional to make the necessary drawing changes without the major expense of redrawing the plans. This package also allows you to print copies of the modified plans as needed. The right of building only one structure from these plans is licensed exclusively to the buyer. You may not use this design to build a second or multiple dwelling(s) without purchasing another blueprint. Each violation of the Copyright Law is punishable in a fine.

MIRROR REVERSE SETS -

Plans can be printed in mirror reverse. These plans are useful when the house would fit your site better if all the rooms were on the opposite side than shown. They are simply a mirror image of the original drawings causing the lettering and dimensions to read backwards. Therefore, when ordering mirror reverse drawings, you must purchase at least one set of right-reading plans. Some of our plans are offered mirror reverse right-reading. This means the plan, lettering and dimensions are flipped but read correctly. See the Home Plans Index on pages 285-286 for availability.

CAD PACKAGES -

A CAD package is a complete set of construction drawings in an electronic file format. They are beneficial if you have a significant amount of changes to make to the home plan or if you need to make the home plan fit your local codes. If you purchase a CAD Package, you can take the plan to a local design professional who uses AutoCAD or DataCAD and they can modify the design much quicker than with a paper-based drawing, which will help save you time and money. Just like our reproducible masters, with a CAD package you will receive a one-time build copyright release that allows you to make changes and the necessary copies needed to build your home. For more information and availability, please call our Customer Service Department at 1-877-379-3420.

Your Blueprint Package will contain the necessary construction information to build your home. We also offer the following products and services to save you time and money in the building process.

MATERIAL LIST

Material lists are available for all of the plans in this book. Each list gives you the quantity, dimensions and description of the building materials necessary to construct your home. You'll get faster and more accurate bids from your contractor while saving money by paying for only the materials you need. See your Commercial Sales Specialist at your local Lowe's Store to receive a free Material List.

EXPRESS DELIVERY

Most orders are processed within 24 hours of receipt. Please allow 7-10 business days for delivery. If you need to place a rush order, please call us by 11:00 a.m. Monday-Friday CST and ask for express service (allow 1-2 business days).

TECHNICAL ASSISTANCE

If you have questions, call our technical support line at 1-314-770-2228 between 8:00 a.m. and 5:00 p.m. Monday-Friday CST. Whether it involves design modifications or field assistance, our designers are extremely familiar with all of our designs and will be happy to help you. We want your home to be everything you expect it to be.

OTHER GREAT PRODUCTS

THE LEGAL KIT -

Avoid many legal pitfalls and build your home with confidence using the forms and contract featured in this kit. Included are request for proposal documents, various fixed price and cost plus contracts, instructions on how and when to use each form, warranty statements and more. Save time and money before you break ground on your new home or start a remodeling project. All forms are reproducible. The kit is ideal for homebuilders and contractors. **Cost: $35.00**

DETAIL PLAN PACKAGES -

Electrical, Plumbing and Framing Packages
Three separate packages offer homebuilders details for constructing various foundations; numerous floor, wall and roof framing techniques; simple to complex residential wiring; sump and water softener hookups; plumbing connection methods; installation of septic systems, and more. Each package includes three dimensional illustrations and a glossary of terms. Purchase one or all three. Note: These drawings do not pertain to a specific home plan.
Cost: $20.00 each or all three for $40.00

(Continued, page 286)

Plan Number	Square Feet	Price Code	Page	Right Read.
535-058D-0058	1,865	C	118	•
535-058D-0063	1,789	B	126	•
535-058D-0064	1,323	A	167	
535-058D-0065	1,512	B	175	
535-058D-0066	1,217	A	187	
535-058D-0067	1,587	B	216	
535-058D-0069	1,207	A	107	
535-058D-0074	676	AAA	239	
535-058D-0078	1,558	B	31	
535-058D-0080	1,428	A	278	
535-058D-0081	1,477	A	132	
535-058D-0083	2,164	C	201	
535-058D-0094	1,895	B	205	
535-058D-0123	1,144	AA	140	
535-058D-0124	1,897	C	221	
535-058D-0127	1,416	A	225	
535-058D-0129	1,217	A	144	
535-058D-0131	751	AAA	229	
535-058D-0132	2,206	D	243	
535-058D-0136	480	AAA	115	•
535-058D-0139	1,240	AAA	148	
535-058D-0141	568	AAA	249	
535-058D-0142	952	AAA	261	
535-058D-0143	665	AAA	270	
535-058D-0144	701	AAA	193	
535-058D-0145	868	AAA	267	
535-058D-0146	868	AAA	154	
535-058D-0151	973	AAA	99	
535-058D-0161	1,993	AA	257	
535-058D-0168	1,568	AA	253	
535-058D-0172	1,635	AA	123	
535-065L-0002	2,101	C	35	
535-065L-0006	2,082	C	17	
535-065L-0013	2,041	C	24	
535-065L-0029	2,077	D	165	•
535-065L-0061	1,498	A	274	•
535-065L-0062	1,390	A	237	•
535-065L-0074	1,640	B	20	•
535-065L-0075	1,727	B	50	•
535-065L-0103	1,860	C	13	
535-065L-0173	1,969	C	190	
535-065L-0192	1,987	C	215	
535-072L-0002	1,767	A	30	
535-072L-0003	1,317	A	23	
535-072L-0007	2,143	C	14	
535-072L-0022	1,891	D	32	
535-072L-0023	1,739	D	27	
535-072L-0024	1,602	D	19	
535-072L-0027	1,820	D	34	
535-072L-0036	1,188	D	11	
535-072L-0049	2,103	E	198	
535-072L-0050	1,941	D	223	
535-072L-0057	1,800	D	246	
535-072L-0058	1,800	D	264	
535-072L-0264	1,556	D	8	
535-072L-0757	1,536	D	182	
535-072L-0759	1,480	C	162	
535-077L-0008	600	A	75	•
535-077L-0042	1,752	C	79	•
535-077L-0074	1,502	C	138	•
535-077L-0097	1,800	D	240	•
535-077L-0128	2,000	C	87	•
535-077L-0142	2,067	D	52	•
535-077L-0156	2,200	D	276	
535-087L-0065	1,384	E	124	
535-087L-0087	1,539	F	142	
535-087L-0095	1,551	F	172	

EXCHANGE POLICIES

Since blueprints are printed in response to your order, we cannot honor requests for refunds. However, if for some reason you find that the plan you have purchased does not meet your requirements, you may exchange that plan for another plan in our collection within 90 days of purchase. At the time of the exchange, you will be charged a processing fee of 25% of your original plan package price, plus the difference in price between the plan packages (if applicable) and the cost to ship the new plans to you. Please note: Reproducible drawings can only be exchanged if the package is unopened.

BUILDING CODES & REQUIREMENTS

At the time the construction drawings were prepared, every effort was made to ensure that these plans and specifications meet nationally recognized codes. Our plans conform to most national building codes. Because building codes vary from area to area, some drawing modifications and/or the assistance of a professional designer or architect may be necessary to comply with your local codes or to accommodate specific building site conditions. We advise you to consult with your local building official for information regarding codes governing your area.

ADDITIONAL SETS*

Additional sets of the plan ordered are available for $45.00 each. Five-set, eight-set, and reproducible packages offer considerable savings.

MIRROR REVERSE PLANS*

Available for an additional $15.00 per set, these plans are simply a mirror image of the original drawings causing the dimensions and lettering to read backwards. Therefore, when ordering mirror reverse plans, you must purchase at least one set of right-reading plans. Some of our plans are offered mirror reverse right-reading. This means the plan, lettering and dimensions are flipped but read correctly. To purchase a mirror reverse right-reading set, the cost is an additional $150.00. See the Home Plans Index on pages 285-286 for availability.

ONE-SET STUDY PACKAGE

We offer a one-set plan package so you can study your home in detail. This one set is considered a study set and is marked "not for construction." It is a copyright violation to reproduce blueprints.

*Available only within 90 days after purchase of plan package or reproducible masters of same plan.

BLUEPRINT PRICE SCHEDULE

BEST VALUE

Price Code	1-Set	Save $80 5-Sets	Save $115 8-Sets	Reproducible Masters
AAA	$310	$410	$510	$610
AA	$410	$510	$610	$710
A	$470	$570	$670	$770
B	$530	$630	$730	$830
C	$585	$685	$785	$885
D	$635	$735	$835	$935
E	$695	$795	$895	$995
F	$750	$850	$950	$1050
G	$1000	$1100	$1200	$1300
H	$1100	$1200	$1300	$1400
I	$1150	$1250	$1350	$1450
J	$1200	$1300	$1400	$1500
K	$1250	$1350	$1450	$1550

Plan prices are subject to change without notice.
Please note that plans are not refundable.

SHIPPING & HANDLING CHARGES

US SHIPPING (AK and HI express only)

	1-4 Sets	5-7 Sets	8 Sets or Reproducibles
Regular (allow 7-10 business days)	$15.00	$17.50	$25.00
Priority (allow 3-5 business days)	$35.00	$40.00	$45.00
Express* (allow 1-2 business days)	$50.00	$55.00	$60.00

CANADA SHIPPING**

Standard (allow 8-12 business days)	$35.00	$40.00	$45.00
Express* (allow 3-5 business days)	$75.00	$85.00	$95.00

*For express delivery please call us by 11:00 a.m. Monday-Friday CST

Overseas Shipping/International - Call, fax, or e-mail (plans@hdainc.com) for shipping costs

**Orders may be subject to custom's fees and or duties/taxes

CAD FORMAT PLANS Many of our plans are available in CAD.
For availability, please call our Customer Service Number below.

1-877-379-3420

HOW TO ORDER

1.) **CALL** toll-free 1-877-379-3420 for credit card orders

2.) **FAX** your order to 1-314-770-2226

3.) **MAIL** the Order Form to: *HDA , Inc.*
944 Anglum Road
St. Louis, MO 63042
ATTN: Customer Service Dept.

For fastest service, Call Toll-Free **1-877-379-3420** day or night

ORDER FORM

Please send me -

PLAN NUMBER 535-_____

PRICE CODE _____ (see pages 285-286)

Specify Foundation Type (see plan page for availability)

☐ Slab   ☐ Crawl space   ☐ Pier

☐ Basement   ☐ Walk-out basement

☐ Reproducible Masters $_____

☐ Eight-Set Plan Package $_____

☐ Five-Set Plan Package $_____

☐ One-Set Study Package (no mirror reverse) $_____

Additional Plan Sets*

☐ ____ (Qty.) at $45.00 each $_____

Mirror Reverse*

☐ Right-reading $150 one-time charge $_____
(see index on pages 285-286 for availability)

☐ Print in Mirror Reverse $_____
(where right-reading is not available)

____ (Qty.) at $15.00 each

☐ Legal Kit (see page 284) (002D-9991) $_____

Detail Plan Packages: (see page 284)

☐ Framing ☐ Electrical ☐ Plumbing $_____
(002D-9992)   (002D-9993)   (002D-9994)

☐ CAD Packages (call for availability and pricing) $_____

SUBTOTAL $_____

Sales Tax (MO residents add 7%) $_____

☐ Shipping / Handling (see chart on page 287) $_____

TOTAL (US funds only - sorry no CODs) $_____

* Available only within 90 days after purchase of plan package
or reproducible masters of the same plan.

I hereby authorize HDA, Inc. to charge this purchase to my credit card account (check one):

☐ MasterCard   ☐ VISA   ☐ DISCOVER   ☐ AMERICAN EXPRESS Cards

Prices are subject to change without notice.
Please note plans are not refundable.

Credit Card number_____

Expiration date _____

Signature _____

Name _____
(Please print or type)

Street Address _____
(Please do not use a PO Box)

_____

City_____

State_____

Zip_____

Daytime phone number   (_____) - _____

E-mail address _____

I am a   ☐ Builder/Contractor
☐ Homeowner
☐ Renter

I ☐ have ☐ have not selected my general contractor

Thank you for your order!